WORLD OF TOYS

LESLIE DAIKEN

A GUIDE TO THE PRINCIPAL PUBLIC AND
PRIVATE COLLECTIONS IN GREAT BRITAIN
OF
PERIOD TOYS : DOLLS AND DOLLS' HOUSES
: GAMES : PUPPETS AND MARIONETTES : TOY
SOLDIERS : MUSICAL BOXES AND AUTOMATA
ALSO
MODERN TOYS : TOYMAKERS AND TOYSHOPS :
PUPPET AND MARIONETTE TROUPES : THE
BRITISH TOY INDUSTRY AND TOY TRADE PRESS.

LAMBARDE
PRESS

1963

© 1963 *The Lambarde Press*

Printed by The Portland Press, London, S.E.25

CONTENTS

PART I

Dolls, Toys, Games & General Juvenilia in Public
Collections in Great Britain   1-69

CONTENTS

PART II

Dolls, Dolls' Houses, Doll Clubs, Special Exhibitions
70-98

PART III

Private Collections of Period Dolls and Toys 99-114

CONTENTS

PART IV

CONTENTS

ILLUSTRATIONS

Unless otherwise stated, original photographs were supplied
by the owners of the objects illustrated.

ILLUSTRATIONS

ILLUSTRATIONS

ACKNOWLEDGMENT

It would be an invidious task to attempt the selection of names from the very long list of those who have contributed information, advice and encouragement to the Author during his compilation of this book; and space considerations prevent the publication of such a list in its entirety.

The Author therefore offers his most grateful thanks to the immense but perforce anonymous army of museum officials, club secretaries, traders and private individuals who responded so enthusiastically to his requests for information, and without whom this book could never have been written.

(xiii)

ACKNOWLEDGMENTS

ADDITIONAL INFORMATION

The following additions and corrections were received after printing had commenced, and were consequently not able to be inserted in their correct places in the text.

Pages 46 and 68. Luton Museum, Maidstone Museum, and the Welsh Folk Museum: —Details of Opening Times were not available at the time of going to Press, but it may be assumed that these Museums are open during all reasonable hours on weekdays.

Page 82. The Batty Dolls' House: —From information recently received, it is understood that Opening Times are now Easter to September, 11 a.m.—9 p.m.
On page 83, line 10, the number of models is amended to 200, and references to Giotto Campanile and St. Paul's Cathedral (lines 16 & 17) should be deleted, as should items 58 and 162 (lines 24, 25 & 29).

Page 115. The two lines commencing "Contributed by Jane Phillips . . ." relate only to the three paragraphs on pages 117-8, and not to the whole of Part IV.

Page 137. Some Television Puppeteers: —Add Sam Williams, creator of "Peter Rabbit and his Friends" for BBC-TV.

Page 154. The list of exhibits was contributed by Major H. Harris.

Page 156. The entry relating to the Royal United Services Institution should now read: —
The R.U.S.I. Museum left Whitehall in August 1963, and all exhibits have been dispersed among the Victoria and Albert Museum, the National Maritime Museum, the

ADDITIONAL INFORMATION—*Continued*

National Army Museum, Camberley, the Imperial War Museum, and the Tower of London. Certain dioramas have been sent to appropriate local Museums, such as York and Hastings.

Page 158. The Hon. Secretary of the British Model Soldier Society is:—A. G. Clayton, 32 Seymour Court, Colney Hatch Lane, London, N.10.

Page 232.

Add:—The Misses Helen and Rosemary Julius, of Stourton Caundle, Sturminster Newton, Dorset (Tel: Stalbridge 324) make an attractive range of toy birds and animals.

PART I

DOLLS, TOYS, GAMES & GENERAL JUVENILIA
IN
PUBLIC COLLECTIONS IN GREAT BRITAIN

Summarising the collections to be found in the following
cities and towns: —

(A) ENGLAND—LONDON
      British Museum.
      Commonwealth Institute.
      Gunnersbury Park Museum.
      Horniman Museum.
      London Museum.
      Science Museum.
      Victoria & Albert Museum/Bethnal Green Museum.
      Wellcome Historical Medical Museum.

(B) ENGLAND—PROVINCES

Alton.	Leeds.
Barnard Castle.	Luton.
Basingstoke.	Maidstone.
Bradford.	Northwood.
Brighton.	Norwich.
Bristol.	Nottingham.
Cambridge.	Oxford.
Chelmsford.	Peterborough.
Colchester.	Rugeley.
Dartford.	St. Ives.
Derby.	Snowshill.
Hereford.	Torquay.
Hove.	Tunbridge Wells.
Keighley.	Warwick
Kew.	Worthing.
Lansdown.	York.

(C) SCOTLAND
    Edinburgh.

    Aberdeen.   Glasgow.

    Blair Atholl.   Kilmarnock.

    Brechin.   Kingussie.

    Dumfries.   South Queensferry.

    Elgin.   Turriff.

(D) WALES
    Cardiff.

    St. Fagan's.   Brecon.

                     Carmarthen.

BRITISH MUSEUM
GREAT RUSSELL STREET, W.C.1.

Opening Times—Summer: *Weekdays, 10—5.*
                                  Sunday, 2.30—6.
             Winter: *Weekdays, 10.30—4.30.*
                                  Sunday, 3—5.30.
              Admission Free.

Exhibits that come within the scope of children's play and entertainment are distributed through this vast national collection, but there is no generic guide, or co-ordinated information, to aid the student or specialist. Many specimens of interest to the latter are kept out of sight through lack of space. The only method of ascertaining fully what material is on view, or in store, is by consulting the Keepers of the respective Departments by correspondence.

Asiatic Saloon

Newly exhibited here are terracotta objects of the Indus Valley Civilisation which have a profound interest to toy historians in view of the recent excavations there.

The Egyptian (IVth) Room

The objects previously seen here, and widely discussed in reference books, were confined to a fraction of the collection of ancient Egyptian specimens for which accommodation could not be found owing to war exigencies. Paddle-dolls, which were formerly grouped in this Room with miscellaneous toys and votive objects, are now elsewhere. The augmented collection has been entirely re-arranged and mounted in a different sequence. About 125 items are now on view and these include the following : —

    Ancient Egyptian board games; table games; counters; dice.

    Dolls and figurines in pottery and wood.

    Fabric throwballs.

    Glazed throwballs and tops.

    Mouse, wooden horse on wheels.

    31 animal heads, terracotta.

Department of Ethnography

This section of the Museum places on view various play-objects related to the tribal or domestic exhibits representing primitive societies from all over the world. They are, as are all other British Museum collections, integrated into the general framework of what is shown—with the exception of the Egyptian and Greek Departments which have grouped and captioned play material specifically under *Games and Toys*.

An examination of the Ethnographic showcases is rewarding, for here may be found fine examples of toy boats with leaf sails and canoes from the Trobriand Islands; bows-and-arrows used by children of certain tribes; and spinning tops of a kind which vividly indicate the principles used in industrially-manufactured versions.

Other votive dolls, figurines, fetishes and tribal symbolic play-objects, include those in natural materials from the Hawaiian, Fiji and Society Islands; Ibibu Tribe, Eastern Nigeria; Zulu and Basuto dolls from South Africa; Zanzibar. From South American countries like Peru and Central Brazil, several specimens are in store, such as pottery dolls from Peru; Pueblo Doll with feather head-dress, $8\frac{1}{2}''$; several specimens of doll made from woven fabrics, twisted cane and coarse woven canvas, the latter with animal designs woven into the material, 16". There are also doll masks from Java.

Here also, may be seen Chinese and Javanese Shadow Puppets. (*See also Part IV*, PUPPETS).

Department of Greek and Roman Antiquities

A newly-arranged show-case in the Room devoted to Greek and Roman Life displays terracotta playthings of ancient Greece and Rome. These range from articulated playdolls 4"-6" high to pull-toys and other toys used by children of these cultures, many having been buried with their small owners.

The present keeper, Mr. D. E. L. Haynes, is always willing to help *bona fide* students, provided that a written request for an appointment is addressed to him.

COMMONWEALTH INSTITUTE
KENSINGTON HIGH STREET, LONDON, W.8.
(Previously known as " The Imperial Institute ")

Opening Times: *Weekdays*, 10—5.30.
Sunday, 2.30—6.

Closed Christmas Eve, Christmas Day and Good Friday.

Admission Free.

The Institute was founded in 1887. Its purpose was then, and is now, to promote a wider knowledge and understanding of the countries and people of the Commonwealth.

The Institute moved to its newly-designed building in 1962. The permanent exhibitions were completely re-designed utilising all the modern techniques now available. The result is one of the most lively and colourful displays to be seen in London.

Sixty thousand square feet of spacious Galleries on three floors present, country by country, a unique survey of the life and environment of all the nations and territories throughout the Commonwealth, ranging from primitive island societies, to the most advanced modern countries.

There is a remarkable series of dioramas and other models to illustrate history; natural resources; industry; social and economic development. Beautifully dressed dolls and figurines display local costumes and there are many beautiful examples of arts and crafts.

Although focus is not upon playthings *qua* toys and games, the visitor will see much material of interest.

GUNNERSBURY PARK MUSEUM
GUNNERSBURY PARK, LONDON, W.3.

Opening Times: *Winter*: *Wednesday, Saturday, Sunday,*
 2—4.
 Summer: *Tuesday, 2 — 5 ; Wednesday,*
 Thursday and Saturday, 11—1,
 2—5.
 Sunday, 3—8.

Brochure available, price 6d.

Dolls

A total of 46 medium and large, of which two are Parisian of C1825, two C1835, several C1860 and one in Elizabethan fancy dress which may be a representation of Princess Alexandra of Wales as Queen Elizabeth (C1890), several of which are known to have been made. One locally made pedlar doll. Twenty-six small dolls of same period, 3 "Dutch" (wooden) and three mechanical dolls. Two sets and several individual pieces of dolls' costumes, hats, etc. Several beautifully dressed dolls in dolls' houses.

Dolls' Houses

One large, with lighting of C1905, on loan; 2 from the locality, C1870.

Dolls' House Furniture

Several pieces not in houses, including some made locally by a clever cabinet maker. Two real apprentice pieces—miniature tables, a doll's writing set, a worktable, a carpenter's table with tools, kitchen equipment, laundry equipment, all mid-19th Cent. or earlier.

Toys, Miscellaneous

Zoëtrope and strips, kaleidoscope, stereoscope (no views). Several sets of early transparencies. Working model steam engine. Rocking horse. A good representative collection of much-used and worn Edwardian toys. One automatic Stollwerck machine. Wooden horses. Tops. Trains. Marbles. Victorian humming top and German Easter Egg.

Table Games

Solitaire and a solitaire with tower. The usual dominoes, halma, table croquet and a fine set of Bristol Glass "woods" for indoor bowls. Twelve table games of C1890—1900, "Wanderer in the Wilderness", incomplete, early 19th Cent. Several Dissected Puzzles (Jig-Saw), pre-1800 and later, including three maps, Cock Robin, Dame School, Bob Cherry, Birds, Life of Christ.

Card Games

Some educational, including Suffragette game of "Panko" of C1912 and five of early 19th Cent.; Two mid-19th Cent. fortune-telling games; Two packs of Nursery playing-cards. making a total of 26 sets.

Building Blocks

Six sets of wood (various). One large set "Richters Anchor" block of composition material; One set miniature baked clay bricks, alphabet and numerals; Two modern (C1950) plastic "don" bricks; One wooden, dated 1847; One thin, intersecting (patent of 1867); One set of various old picture blocks, C1830.

Toy Soldiers

Field Hospital, about 1914—tent, beds, etc. About 300 items, mostly in sets and most in good condition. Infantry, cavalry, camel corps, Guards, Scots regiment, guns, including one complete field-gun detachment. None are in khaki.

Aeroplane

Toy clockwork monoplane with rear propeller, much damaged.

Trains

Five, some incomplete, one believed early.

Writing Sheets and Picture Sheets, from C1800

Subjects—Life of Christ; Miracles of Christ; Two writing sheets; Three copy books.

Greeting Cards

Packets of over 100 Christmas and Greeting Cards sent to a child, C1878.

Scrap Books
Polyphon and Records

HORNIMAN MUSEUM
LONDON ROAD, FOREST HILL, S.E.23.

Opening Times: *Weekdays (except Monday), 10.30—6.*
Sunday, 2—6.
Open Good Friday and Bank Holidays.
Admission Free.

Ethnographical collections display the arts and crafts of man in all parts of the world, and objects illustrating magic, art and religion. There is also a large collection of musical instruments, both European and exotic. The museum has a large reference library.

There are more than 120 dolls exhibited and many others in store. The collection is from all over the world, from early Egyptian C1500 B.C., Ancient Mexico C200 A.D., and Ancient Peru, up to modern times.

The toys include simple specimens of clay, made by the children, to the more elaborate ones from China, Japan and India. A special section is devoted to animal toys from many lands. There is a complete set of the dolls of the Girls' Festival "Hi No Matsuri" of ancient origin, Japan; and rag dolls from Burma. English and Continental dolls are included in the display. Natural materials from which the dolls are made, include: wood, clay, leather, bone, fur, cheese, straw, papier-mâché.

There is also a section of puppets from Europe (Belgium, England and Sicily), Africa (Western Sudan), Asia (Burma, Java, Cambodia and Siam). The marionettes can be set in motion in the case. Some of the dolls have dual purposes, being also used for magical purposes.

8

The game section includes Battledore bats from London (C1700), Japan and W. Africa. Balls from many countries made from dried fruit, palm leaves, stoneware, ivory, plaited rattan. Diabolo spool with sticks (England), tops from Ancient Egypt (made of clay), India, Maldive Islands, Lipari, Aeolian Islands, Italy (all made of wood); and stone and wooden ones from New Guinea.

Among the large collection of musical instruments are children's musical toys from many lands.

LONDON MUSEUM
KENSINGTON PALACE,

THE BROAD WALK, KENSINGTON GARDENS, W.8.

Opening Times: *March to September*: *Weekdays,* 10—6
Sunday, 2—6.
October to February: *Weekdays,* 10—4.
Sunday, 2—4.

Closed Christmas Eve, Christmas Day and Good Friday.

Until 1912 the greatest city in this country had no Museum illustrating the story of its own past. In that year the London Museum was founded to show the daily life and history of London through the centuries. Because there have always been children in the city's houses and streets, there have been children's toys in the Museum since its first opening. The oldest playthings are probably the Roman games, counters, and dice which are as important in reconstructing our picture of *Londinium* as the great amphorae for imported wine or the strigil for use at the public baths.

The Museum originally had its home in Kensington Palace and was inaugurated there by King George V and Queen Mary, who took a great interest in the building up of this new Museum's collections. They lent many of their own interesting and precious possessions and among these were numerous toys and dolls. So it was that Queen Victoria's collection of 132 little wooden dolls were among the items which delighted visitors in the early days of the Museum. Just as a small group of people often tends to attract others to become a crowd, in the same way a few toys grew in number and became an interesting collection as visitors remembered their own childhood possessions in drawers and attics and resolved to give them to the Museum. Perhaps Royal toys have special powers of attraction! The majority of items have been acquired by gift rather than purchase.

In 1914 Lancaster House became the Museum's second home, where it remained until its collections had to be stored for protection during the Second World War. It was re-opened at Kensington Palace in 1951, where its toy collection has become so large that only a small proportion of items can be exhibited at any one time.

The total collection comprises well over 2,000 items covering every aspect of toys, dolls and games, including the following: —

Dolls, etc.
Over 220 dolls dated from 1700 onwards.
Five dolls' houses completely furnished, the earliest dated 1837.
Dolls' prams and wooden toys pulled by strings such as animals, motor cars and steam engines.
Dolls' cots, cradles, beds and similar accessories.

Toys, miscellaneous
Two Pollock Theatres plus scenes and dialogues for 10 players.
A range of seven scooters, the earliest C1850, the latest 1935.
Three tricycles dated 1910.
One aeroplane-scooter dated 1914.
Two Noah's Arks.
Two fully equipped farmyards, each with a full set of animals.

Toy soldiers, sailors, Red Indians, etc., in lead, plus moulds for making the same, *circa* 1900 and 1913.

Several sets of railway engines, carriages, lines, etc., including a dozen carriages made in 1880.

Children's musical instruments of every description.

A very large and comprehensive range of mechanical toys made of metal and a good many examples of mechanical toys made of wood.

Several musical boxes.

Collection of musical automata, gramophones, etc.

Magic lanterns, cinematographs and similar equipment.

Scrap albums, cut-out paper dolls.

Games and Sports Equipment

Knur and spell; cricket; croquet; archery; skating; curling; hawking, cock-fighting; fishing; golf; tennis; bowls; skittles; marbles and equipment, etc.; 27 board games; 22 card games; 35 jig-saw puzzles; several chess, domino and draught sets; very many boxes of building bricks ranging from infants upwards.

Early construction kits, including Tinker Toy, Cliptico, Meccano and several un-named sets, *circa* 1880.

Conjuring, chemistry and electrical kits.

Card sets such as "The Little Ship-builder"; "The Little Carpenter"; "The Little Smith".

Children's Books

Over three hundred juvenile books.

The Museum, of which the Director is Dr. D. B. Harden, publishes for sale a charming illustrated booklet entitled *Toys and Games*. This was compiled by the Children's Officer, Miss Helen Young, who also gives lecture-demonstrations on toys to School groups. Illustrations are by Mr. A. S. Trottman, Staff Photographer, and include pictures of English wax dolls, toy musical boxes, one of the oldest Rocking Horses known in England, and sand-operated and gas-operated toys of movement. Playthings presented by Queen Mary are a special attraction.

11

Other famous collections on view at the London Museum include: —

The King Collection of Penny Toys

The London Museum acquired many of its toys from grown-up collectors. Mr. Ernest King, for example, presented over 1,600 little "Penny Toys"—each one different—which he himself bought fifty years ago from street-hawkers near Ludgate Hill.

Queen Victoria's Dolls

Of special interest to doll collectors is a show-case of some of Queen Victoria's own dolls—dolls that she bought with her pennies as a child and dressed herself. Only about thirty of the one hundred and thirty-two survivors of her childhood are at present displayed, but the curator of the Museum will gladly show the others to anyone having more than a casual interest.

They are nearly all of carved wood or wax, and most of them are the inexpensive kind that could then (the 1820's) have been bought for as little as 2d. or 3d. (three or four cents American). The wooden ones have crudely painted faces and are jointed. In some, at least, a considerable amount of work must have gone into the carving of the heads, which are glazed to give an appearance of china. The dolls are approximately six or seven inches in height.

The complete history of these dolls and how they came to be named after people known to the young Princess and her Governess, is told in a charming book, *Queen Victoria's Dolls*, by Frances H. Low. Although published in 1894, and long since out of print, it is not rare, and for those who can come across a copy, or can borrow one, a study of the exhibits is made all the more rewarding by comparing the originals with the water-colour illustrations by Alan Wright which lavishly adorn the volume.

SCIENCE MUSEUM
EXHIBITION ROAD, SOUTH KENSINGTON, LONDON, S.W.7.

Opening Times: *Weekdays* 10—6.
Sunday 2.30—6.
Science Library, Weekdays only, 10—5.30.

Admission Free.

The Science Museum, South Kensington, has, at the time of writing, no collection of toys as such, but toys have played a small part in the history of science and engineering and are consequently represented in the collections here and there. For instance, there is a good collection of Zoëtropes shown working in the Cinematography gallery, and the small portable orreries in the Astronomy gallery are instructive toys rather than scientific instruments.

Special interest attaches to the George III Collection of scientific apparatus collected in the 18th century for the education of the Royal children. These objects are not toys, but many were devised specially for young people and are forerunners of the scientific toys of the late 19th century.

The manufacture of scientific toys designed to be instructive as well as amusing seems to have begun in earnest late in the 18th century and perhaps the most beautiful of such toys were the portable orreries. They must be classed as toys, for the complete disregard for true proportion rules out their having any use as instruments, and they were made in some quantity, the chart on the table top being printed (on vellum). These extremely elegant constructions in brass, in ivory and mahogany symbolized the 18th century concept of the whole man and gave the growing boy no excuse for thinking in terms of two cultures. The orrery remained popular well into the 19th century and its popularity probably only declined in the face of the superior attractions of the toy steam-engine. Now that the real steam-engine is disappearing from the public eye, and with the new possibilities of interplanetary travel, the orrery is ripe for revival—no doubt in plastic form!

13

In its first fifty years the toy steam-engine was hand-built and only for the sons of the rich. The orrery employed the techniques of clockmaking, but there was no comparable tradition that could be applied to the making of small boilers and cylinders. Consequently many of the early pieces are models rather than toys but, with the arrival of the locomotive, with its immense popular appeal and what might fairly be called its vivid personality, the potential market expanded and cheap models were being made, still by hand, by about 1870.

None of the toys of this period are accurate but all are pleasing. The elaborate ones, built to a large scale, reflect the grace of the real locomotives of the day and are extremely well-made, with fully modelled link motion and a great deal of characteristic detail. They were very largely constructed of brass castings, elaborately painted and with much bright brass, copper and steel, but were more lightly built than the real thing. The cheap models were never painted and took all sorts of liberties with the outline of the locomotive. Oscillating cylinders, very tall chimneys and the minimum four wheels seem to have been the rule, together with classical names redolent of the very early days of railways: *Vulcan*, *Ajax* or *Hercules*. The special charm of these cheap models lies in the way they capture the essence of the steam locomotive. They represent no particular engine but they represent all engines, and one of these toys in action is infinitely more realistic than any of the small electrically-driven models of steam locomotives which one can buy today. They are also far more instructive and, as they demand more attention and some skill to get the best out of them, their "play value" is high.

I am indebted to the Museum Lecturer, Mr. J. T. Van Riemsdijk, whose lecture-demonstrations on Scientific Toys are a feature of the Christmas holidays, for the foregoing information.

VICTORIA AND ALBERT MUSEUM
CROMWELL ROAD, SOUTH KENSINGTON, S.W.7.

Opening Times: Weekdays, 10—6.
Sunday, 2.30—6.

Admission Free.

The Stone Collection

The Victoria and Albert Museum received a few years ago a most generous gift of the complete collection of Juvenile Drama material which Mr. M. W. Stone spent almost sixty years gathering together. This valuable acquisition consists of more than two hundred texts of the plays used in performances of the miniature theatre as well as thousands of sheets, both plain and coloured, of scenery and characters, examples of the work of all the known publishers of this form of theatrical entertainment issued between 1811 and 1900.

This collection is the third to be acquired by one of our national museums and covers a wider range than the Ralph Thomas Collection at the British Museum or the King Collection at the London Museum. It is also provided with a typewritten catalogue by whose aid quick reference may be made to the illustrations of famous Regency and Early Victorian Dramas and Pantomimes.

Among the items of particular interest are sheets published by West in 1811, also three which show the W.B. monogram, at one time claimed to be the initials of William Blake. Other sheets show the likeness of Liston, Farley and other actors of the early 19th century, whilst some of the pantomime sheets portray Grimaldi and other famous members of the harlequinade. There are also many playbills of performances in the patent theatres of plays from which the publishers took their versions of Juvenile Drama.

The Barnett Collection

The bulk of the exhibits come from the collection of Mr. Raymond Barnett, which was bought for the Museum in 1954 with the help of an anonymous benefactor.

Mr. Barnett was collecting from 1930 to 1954 and many of his best things were found in country towns. His greatest stroke of good fortune was at Tewkesbury in 1941, where he found a small haberdasher's shop, kept by a Miss Reeves, who was the great-niece of the man who, in 1846, had founded the business as a "Fancy Repository". Part of the original stock of toys and games was still there.

Mr. Barnett bought about 50 items and would have bought more, but Miss Reeves died in 1944 aged 83, and unhappily the remainder of the "Fancy Repository" stock was thrown away.

Among the things from this shop which are stored in the collection is a small German clockwork train (engine, tender, and passenger coach) which is possibly the earliest surviving toy of its kind. It still works perfectly. Another great rarity from the same source is the *"Anorthoscope"*—one of the earliest toys which create the illusion of moving pictures.

One of the earliest exhibits is a child's writing-case of about 1780. It is an enchanting thing of French manufacture, with tiny envelopes and sheets of paper (all having hand-painted decoration), sealing-wax of several colours, and blue and silver dusting powder, and is an almost miraculous example of preservation.

The Mansion of Happiness, published in 1800, shows the extreme skill and perseverance with which Mr. Barnett worked, for he was able to bring together, all from different sources, the artist's original design, two proof states, the first published edition, and a reprint of half a century later—a record it would be hard to equal with material so ephemeral and perishable as this.

Old jig-saws and picture blocks, some of the early 19th century examples which enabled the child to put together pic-

tures of truly remarkable pseudo-Egyptian structures, form
another interesting group. There are also peep-shows, tumbling clowns worked by gravity, and the *"Panoramacopia"* of
1824.

This was invented by a certain "T. T. Dales, Drawing
Master", an obscure artist, possibly, but clearly one of much
charm and skill. It consists of several upright aquatints which
can be grouped in every possible way each time to form a
different landscape. A pretty toy indeed—but then the same
is true of a hundred other things in the exhibition, which
carries the story of children's parlour games down to about
1860 and the "Happy Families" cards designed by Sir John
Tenniel.

(*See also page* 71 *for* DOLLS.)

BETHNAL GREEN MUSEUM
CAMBRIDGE HEATH ROAD, E.2.
Opening Times: Weekdays, 10—6.
Sunday, 2.30—6.

Admission Free.

The Museum is a branch of the Victoria and Albert
Museum.

One half of the lower south gallery is occupied by cases displaying dolls, dolls' houses, models, etc., mostly chosen from
the children's section which became a distinctive feature of
Bethnal Green Museum between the World Wars. The other
half contains British furniture and small woodwork objects,
together with specimens of woods used by cabinet-makers. A
"ribband-back" chair, very similar to one illustrated in the
first edition (1754) of Thomas Chippendale's trade publication, *The Gentleman and Cabinet-Maker's Director,* is perhaps the most noteworthy single item in the collection.
Miniature furniture and English wallpapers of different
periods are shown in the wall-cases.

The great variety of toys at Bethnal Green (other than dolls and dolls' houses) comprises a remarkable rocking horse, Noah's Ark, Geographical Panorama, Pollock Theatre, "Prince Charles" British Railways clockwork locomotive (1959) from Messrs. Bassett-Lowke, two interesting series of toy soldiers and a modern model circus.

The two new (1960) Victoria and Albert Museum picture books are useful additional reminders of what there is at Bethnal Green. In the *Dolls' Houses* picture book of 28 plates, Nos. 2, 4—6, 11—20 and 25—28 are here. In the *Dolls* picture book, plates 8, 10, 12, 14, 16, 20, 23-25, 27 and 28 are at Bethnal Green.

Dolls of ethnographic interest include one from Peru made of coarse canvas, its dress embroidered with beads and black hair, $13\frac{1}{2}''$; an Eskimo Doll of carved whalebone, $3''$; a masked Indian dancer doll from Bolivia, 1859, 18".

Museum policy is not to exhibit at any one time more than a proportion of its rich children's collection. At regular intervals special Exhibitions of juvenile interest are mounted. Wide interest was occasioned by the Exhibition of Puppetry and Toy Theatre (December, 1954-February, 1955), now incorporated into the Library of the Victoria and Albert Museum —(*see page* 143 *under* PUPPETS)—and an Exhibition of Transport Models (1961) telling the story of public conveyances from the early diligence and the horse-omnibus, to electric trams and all stages of motor omnibuses.

A generous loan from the British Transport Commission's Museum comprised buses, trains and boats, designed for a variety of purposes, a series supplemented by trams, 1880-1952, lent through the Tramway and Light Railway Society's good offices.

Lilliputian railways have long bulked large in boyhood's Christmas and birthday visions. The exhibition owed much to Dr. A. C. Stossel's kindness in lending from his fine collection of toy trains.

WELLCOME HISTORICAL MEDICAL MUSEUM
THE WELLCOME BUILDING,
EUSTON ROAD, LONDON, N.W.1.

Opening Times: *Monday to Friday*, 10—5.
                   Closed Bank Holidays and Week-ends.
Admission Free.

The collection was founded by Sir Henry Wellcome. It illustrates the history of medicine and allied sciences from the earliest times to the present century. Selected material and special exhibitions, which are changed from time to time, are open to the public.

Among the primitive dolls, votive objects, figurines and playthings of ethnographical interest are the following: —

Africa

Ashanti Dolls, of dark wood, wearing beads.

North American Indian

Papoose in a baby-carrier, collected in the U.S.A. by Sir Henry Wellcome.

Katchina Indian: baby doll attached to flat cradle-board.

The space available to the Museum is, at the present time, very limited and it is possible to exhibit only a small part of the collections, including the ethnographical dolls etc. The material on exhibition is changed from time to time. As far as possible, arrangements are made for scholars to consult particular parts of the collection, which are not on exhibition, but this facility cannot be extended to general visitors.

THE CURTIS MUSEUM
HIGH STREET, ALTON, HAMPSHIRE.

Open Weekdays, except Bank and Public Holidays
                   June to September, 10—5.30
                   October to May, 10—5.
                   Closes 1 *p.m. on Wednesday.*

This Museum, administered by the Hampshire Education Committee, has a small collection of toys, as part of the "Bygones" section. They come mainly under the heading of *dolls* and *games*, and the majority were acquired either as having local association or as being the type that local children would have been likely to have, though a small number of foreign costume dolls have been given from time to time.

Most items date from the 19th or early 20th centuries, but one doll is mid-18th century and is complete with clothes, including a change of dress. Other single objects of some interest are a late-Victorian money-box in the from of a slot machine; the child being able to extract a sweet for each coin inserted, and a doll's house of the same or slightly earlier date (of which post-card photographs are sold). There is also a set of dolls' house furniture made from feathers.

There are several educational games such as jig-saws forming maps and Bible scenes, and examples of children's schoolroom handiwork, including a collection of samplers.

THE BOWES MUSEUM
BARNARD CASTLE, Co. DURHAM.
Open Weekdays, 10—5.30; 1st May to 1st September.

Admission, 1/-; Children, 6d.

The Bowes Museum in Barnard Castle is remarkable for the grandeur of its building and the magnificence of its collections.

John Bowes, the founder, born on the 19th of June, 1811, was the son of the 10th Earl of Strathmore, of Streatlam Castle, and Mary Milner, of Stainton, and all who visit the Museum and Park cannot fail to experience a sense of gratitude for the munificence and public spirit which animated John Bowes and his wife. They have provided an institution which can be enjoyed by all and it provides a stimulus to the appreciation of beautiful things.

On sale is a well-illustrated descriptive handbook giving a Room-by-Room account of objects in the 22 Rooms, of which the toys are in Room 19, The Children's Room, which leads from the 16th-century room. In this are to be seen several doll's houses. One of them was presented by Mrs. Bell. Near it are collections of dolls. Those in European national costumes were given by Mrs. R. P. Summerson, the English dolls by Miss Ida Headlam and another by Mrs. A. Richardson. The large Doll's House in the centre of the floor is furnished as a period house with a 17th-century dining room, an 18th-century drawing room, rooms of the period C1820, and modern. Tiny silver table dishes, glass and porcelain, are set out and miniature pictures are on the walls. Small figures in costume occupy the rooms. Another doll's house is nearby, and is furnished in a similar way. The outside is said to be a model of the house built by Henry Norris in 1509 (see the initials and date), who was executed for supposed intrigue with Anne Boleyn.

A group of wax figures in Slavonic costume of the 17th century make up a wedding scene. The group is said to have belonged to one of the Kings of Bavaria.

This group and the two dolls' houses were bequeathed by Lady Surtees of Mainsforth.

Another interesting group is the German early 18th century kitchen, complete with over 100 miniature pewter plates, dishes, etc. Ship models include the first screw collier, the *John Bowes,* and a Trinity House cutter. There are some examples of various types of engines and a railway engine and tender bequeathed by the late H. G. T. Barningham.

In one of the floor cases is a silver swan mounted on glass rods. When it is in motion the glass rods give the impression of moving water and the swan bends its head to grab the fishes. The model was made in England in the 18th century by a man named Weekes and was sent to the Paris exhibition in 1867, where it was purchased by Napoleon III for the Prince Imperial.

THE WILLIS MUSEUM
BASINGSTOKE, HANTS.

Administered by the County's Education Committee, this Museum has a modest, but interesting collection of playthings. Among these are: —

Toys, which include a toy train, C1835-1840.

Dolls which range from C1810-1900.

Dolls' Furniture, including some wooden furniture made in Norway. The rest is of English make and is probably late 19th century. Doll's cradle made of cane, date unknown.

Games, including jig-saw puzzles; also puzzle blocks and building bricks which belonged to the Chute family of the Vyne, Sherborne St. John.

Musical boxes, including one in the form of a doll with a turned wood handle, dressed as a jester.

Children's books, English and French, C1850-1880.

Scrapbooks, which include several compiled by children of the Chute family in the early 1850s, with cuttings about the Relief of Lucknow and the Crimean War, interspersed with Valentines and birthday cards.

Optical amusements include a Fantascope, 1833; **Wallis's Wheel of Wonder**, C1830; Zoëtrope, 1860; Stereoscopes; **Magic Lantern** slides illustrating children's stories and moving pictures painted on glass, activated by a geared handle, date unknown.

BOLLING HALL MUSEUM
BRADFORD 4, YORKS.

Open Daily, 10—8, *April—September.*

10—7, *January—March.*

10—5, *October—December.*

Admission Free.

This Museum has a representative toy collection, which includes some early educational items; about 30 dolls (and dolls' clothing), two of which are probably late 18th century.

There is a growing number of children's books, including one or two items also of 18th century date.

There is one Doll's House and a very large collection of Doll's House furniture and associated objects.

THE TOY MUSEUM
THE GRANGE, ROTTINGDEAN, BRIGHTON, SUSSEX.

*(Honorary Secretary : Stephen Garrett, M.A., A.R.I.B.A.,
17 Conduit Street, London, W.1.)*

Opening Times: *Weekdays, 10—7.*
                 Sundays, 2—7 (closes at 6 p.m. in winter).

Admission Free.   *Guide to the Collection, price 6d.*

This display has been formed from the collections of "The Toy Museum", a private organization which has for many years been collecting children's toys and exhibiting them throughout Britain. After the inaugural exhibition at Devereux Court, Strand, W.C.2 (1953), the home of founder-Trustees Mr. and Mrs. A. Rye, the collection stayed for one year at Leighton House, Kensington; City Art Gallery, Manchester; Leicester City Museum; and Hove Museum; extending its scope all the time. It has been in Rottingdean since 1958.

The collection is on loan to Brighton Corporation and is shown at The Grange, Rottingdean, which is a branch of the Brighton Public Libraries, Art Gallery and Museums. It is hoped that the toy collection will be permanently established in Brighton.

The display is changed from time to time during the year, chiefly at Christmas, Easter and for the summer holidays, and is arranged by Miss Yootha Rose, a Trustee of the Toy Museum.

23

There could be no more fitting home for the collection than this gracious 18th-century mansion overlooking the still waters of the village pond, for the house once belonged to Sir William Nicholson, the artist who designed the original settings for Sir James Barrie's immortal children's play, *Peter Pan*. And a glance at the nostalgic little Museum makes it clear that, in spite of the grown-ups' constant search for the new and the novel, the toys that children love most have changed little through the years. Here you will find rocking horses, dolls and dolls' houses, toy vehicles and miniature villages, games and puzzles—all the treasures of the nurseries and playrooms of long ago.

The toys are admirably grouped according to type. In the first showcase, for instance, are toys that are animated by spring or string, while beside it is a case devoted to the next stage of movement, the clockwork toy. Then there are wheel toys, and examples of the penny toys on sale during the reigns of Queen Victoria and King Edward VII. And an appropriate exhibit is a reproduction of a famous painting by the great 16th-century Flemish artist, Peter Breughel the Elder, which reveals on close inspection as many as seventy toys, games and pastimes in common use four hundred years ago. The picture was painted in 1560 and was intended to provide a record of contemporary life.

In a battered oblong box, is a game that goes back into antiquity, labelled "Ye Olde Greek Game of Knucklebones", and one is reminded of the terracotta figures entitled "Women Playing Knucklebones" which may be seen in the British Museum, London. Dating from 300 B.C. and of South Italian Greek origin, these two terracotta women, representatives of a civilisation long past, are holding knucklebones exactly similar to those in the box at Rottingdean and playing the ancient game with a delightful air of gravity.

In a nearby showcase there is a reconstructed Victorian beach scene. Here are Victorian dolls, primly dressed and seated on a shingle beach with a backstage picture which convinces one that a Victorian beach in summer was a very crowded place indeed. Large-wheeled bathing carts loom in the background, a vendor of knick-knacks displays his tray of wares, and gallants equipped with cane and top hat escort ladies whose voluminous skirts trail among the sand and pebbles in a manner guaranteed to ruin any hem.

Toys that teach are the next group to be encountered, and among these there is a jig-saw puzzle depicting the kings and queens of England, starting with William the Conqueror and ending with King George III (1760-1820), who was presumably occupying the throne at the time the puzzle was made.

But it is often the little home-made objects that are of special appeal, such as a tiny tool box made by Lewis Carroll (author of *Alice in Wonderland*) for his sister Elizabeth. Dated 1846, it was left by Elizabeth to her sister Louisa, then by her to her niece, Frances Meneta Dodgson. The box contains eighty tiny wooden tools, each about an inch in length and just about the right size for Alice after she had swallowed the contents of the bottle labelled "Drink me"—and shrank until she almost disappeared altogether. Another tiny exhibit is a minute hand-made pair of stockings affixed to a card, which bears a neatly written inscription: "Harriet Lyne, aged 14. London Orphan Asylum, 1837". Who was Harriet Lyne, and how did she fare in the years ahead? How one would like to know!

There are, of course, examples of marionettes and glove puppets, as well as a Punch and Judy set and a Pollock's toy theatre (the latter over a hundred years old) with its sheets of characters "Penny plain and tuppence coloured"; and there are also representative toys of many lands—from India, Egypt, Malaya, Jamaica, China, Japan, Russia and Switzerland.

Among the dolls is one with a special claim to fame—it is said to be a model of the Duke of Windsor as a baby. And beside a Teddy Bear exhibit there are some interesting notes on the origin of the name of this nursery favourite. It seems that the first teddy bear was made in 1902 by a Russian immigrant to the United States, Maurice Michton, following the return of President Theodore Roosevelt with a pet bear cub from a hunting expedition in the Rockies. The cub was depicted in a cartoon entitled "Teddy's Bear", and this gave Michton the idea. He made up a stuffed bear, displayed it in a shop window, and was immediately inundated with orders. He then sent the original stuffed bear to the White House with a request that its replicas might be named "Teddy Bear", to which the President promptly replied: "I don't think my name is likely to be worth much in the bear business, but you are welcome to use it".

But among all these toys of the past the products of the modern craftsmen have not been forgotten. There is a gay little reproduction of a Gypsy caravan, sparkling with fresh-coloured ornamentation, and a delightful roundabout made from painted empty cotton-reels—which shows what some can do with objects that others throw away. In the same category are ships made from walnut shells and a small wooden soap box, with sliding lid, that has been converted into a doll's house with two floors. What charming exhibits these will make when they become the bygones of tomorrow!

BLAISE CASTLE FOLK MUSEUM
HENBURY, BRISTOL.

Opening Times: *May to September*:   *Weekdays, 2—6.*
                                                    Sunday, 2—5.
                  October to April: *Weekdays, 2—4.30.*
                                                    Sunday, 3—4.30.
Admission Free.

The Folk Museum, a branch of the City Museum, Bristol, is housed in a late 18th-century mansion, four miles north-west of Bristol. The grounds and the long winding carriage drive through the woods were designed by Humphrey Repton, the landscape artist, in 1796.

The house was opened as a Folk Museum in 1949 and contains exhibits illustrating English life in former days.

The collections range in date from the 15th to 19th centuries and the juvenilia include dolls, musical boxes, and Valentines.

CAMBRIDGE & COUNTY FOLK MUSEUM
2 & 3 CASTLE STREET, CAMBRIDGE.

Open: *Weekdays, 11—1, 2.30—4.30. (Closed Mondays.)*
Sunday, 2.30—4.30.

Admission: *Adults, 6d. Children, 3d.*

The Museum was opened in 1936 and contains exhibits gathered only from the City and County of Cambridge and the Isle of Ely, illustrating the life, work and history of the people of these districts from mediaeval times to the commencement of the 20th century.

There are ten separate rooms filled with bygones. Rooms No. 6 and No. 7 are devoted exclusively to juvenile material, much of which is of general interest, but including several toys and nursery play-articles belonging to the Cambridgeshire region, and having their own local story which the Curator, Miss Enid Porter, is always pleased to recount.

The total collection is listed as follows: —

China, for use by child
> Child's Plate, with coloured transfer print of the Peep-show Man, early 19th cent.
> Nursery Food Warmer, white glazed earthenware, 18th cent.

China, miniature, for dolls' houses
> Dinner and Tea Services, various, in flowered and sprigged china, 19th cent.
> Gilt China Tea Set with matching tray.
> Miniature Vases, Jugs, Bedroom Ware, etc.

Dolls

Collection of 19th and early 20th cent. dolls, mostly in original dress; wax and china faces. One doll, 1810, with wax face, arms and legs, is 2' 6" tall.

Pedlar Doll.

Rag Dolls, various.

Wooden Dolls, of various sizes from $\frac{1}{2}$" to 18" high.

All-china Dolls of various sizes from $\frac{1}{4}$" to 4" high.

Japanese Doll.

Early 18th cen.t or late 17th cent. painted wooden doll, in form of rattle; probably of mid-European origin but found under floor boards of a 16th cent. cottage in Cambridge.

Dolls' Beds and Cradles

Wooden cradle made in 1846 by village carpenter of West Wratting, Cambs.

Small wicker cradle, length 10". 1880.

White painted iron swinging cradle with curtains, 1900.

Drop-sided wooden cot, 1902.

Two mahogany half-tester beds, with curtains. 18th cent.

Four poster bed, carpenter-made, with curtains, C1850.

Dolls' Furniture

Collection of miniature furniture, kitchen and cooking equipment for dolls' houses, 19th and early 20th cent.

Carpenter-made kitchen dresser, C1870. Height 17", width 13", depth $7\frac{1}{2}$".

Cambridge-made hooded basket chair. Height 15".

Armchair, oak with rush seat. Height of back, 18".

Dolls' Houses

Five 19th century houses, three at least carpenter-made; of varying design and size. The largest is 3' x 2' 4" x 1' 6"; the smallest is 1' 10" x 11" x 6". All open in front and are of two or three floors.

Edwardian-type Villa, bought in a Cambridge shop. Front opening gives access to rooms; side opening gives access to hall, stairs and landing. 2' 4" x 1' 6" x 1' 8".

Dolls' Perambulators

Iron-framed and iron-wheeled perambulator with carriage suspended on leather straps. Handle back and front, reversible hood. Holds two dolls, face to face. C1870.

Pushchair, wood and cane, C1880.

Nursery Furniture

Chairs

High Chairs, four; oak and mahogany, each with foot step and guard rail.

Upright chair, oak with cane seat. 1840.

Mahogany chair, upright, with red velvet seat. 1840.

Cradles

Mahogany rocking cradle, with hood. Early 19th cent.

Rocking cradle, with hood, from Madingley Hall, Cambridge. Wood, covered with red velvet, interior lined and padded in white cotton; three feather mattresses. Cover is 18th cent., but cradle itself may well be earlier.

Swinging cradle, mahogany, with cane sides and hood. Stand has brass finials and brass bands to feet. 19th cent.

Walking Aids

Baby Runner, 18th century; wood, painted green. Circular frame, for holding child, attached to (incomplete) upright pole.

Walking Frame, oak, with sliding frame for holding child. Length 3', height 17", width 15"

Circular Runner on wheels; wood, with padded and covered top. Diam. of top, 12"; of base, 2' 2".

Clothes Airer, wood, with metal hooks for attaching to fire guard.

Nursery Pictures, various. These included a framed " Etiquette for Young Folks ", C1870, and a framed Alphabet: " The Comical Hotch Potch or the Alphabet turn'd Posture Master ", printed by Carrington Bowles, 1782.

Perambulators

Go Cart or Mail Cart; wood, iron wheels, padded seat. C1840.

Go Car, or Mail Cart; wood, iron wheels. Two seats, back to back, not padded. Formerly used at the Workhouse, Linton, Cambridgeshire.

Samplers (These are in the Domestic Crafts Room)

Collections of samplers worked by Cambridgeshire children, aged 8 to 13, in the 19th century. Most of them are dated and several bear the names of local schools. The collection includes two needlework pictures worked by children.

Schoolroom Equipment

Teachers' Desk and Cane, early 19th cent., from the village school, Horseheath, Cambs.

Globes, a number of; 18th and 19th cent.

Abacus.

Back Boards, late 18th and early 19th cent., for straightening girls' shoulders.

Pencil Boxes and writing equipment, 19th century.

Toys and Games

A collection of various 18th, 19th and early 20th century toys and games, including: —

Zoëtrope.

Kaleidoscope.

Magic Lanterns and Slides.

Penny Toys, including three " match box toys ".

Noah's Arks (2). The larger of these is 2′ 8″ long.

Tops, collection of, various sizes.

Dray and horses, wood and plaster, in stable. German, but bought in Cambridge in 1930.

Model horse on wheels, 12″ long; covered with calf-skin. 1870.

Motor car, metal; 1908. Length 6".

Wooden engine, L.B. & S.C.R., with two trucks. 1880.

Brass piston engine, "Aeriel". 1890.

Engine, tender and carriage, painted tin. 1860.

Money box in form of chocolate machine. 1890.

Wooden model of gypsy caravan, C1900. 9" x 6" x 4".

Wooden model of a musical instrument seller's shop, 6" x 4". This was salvaged from a toy shop during the fire of 1849 in the Market Place, Cambridge.

Lead soldiers, various.

Pop Gun, French manufacture.

Solitaire and marbles.

Battledore and shuttlecock.

Bat and Trap.

Stilts.

Metal "Blondin"—tight-rope walker.

Cut-out doll with attachable dresses and accompanying story of "Little Fanny", 1813.

In addition to the above the Museum possesses a large number of illustrated children's books of the 19th and early 20th centuries and a collection of school books, including some exercise books, of the same date. There are also a number of table games, such as "The Cottage of Content", etc., card games, bricks and picture blocks, puzzles, together with various educational "aids". These latter include arithmetic and spelling cards, Scripture cards, writing copy books, etc. As well as the samplers listed above the Museum has also various examples of children's needlework and plain sewing, darning, knitting, etc., most of which were prize-winning entries in the school children's needlework competitions held in Cambridge in the last century.

Exhibits in the two children's rooms are changed from time to time to allow as many as possible to be shown in turn; application to see any item not on view may be made to the Curator.

CHELMSFORD AND ESSEX MUSEUM
OAKLANDS PARK, CHELMSFORD, ESSEX.

Open: *Weekdays*: *April to September*, 10—1; 2—7.
  October to March, 10—1; 2—5.
  Sunday: *April to September only*, 2—5.

Recent acquisitions include a collection of twelve toys belonging to the Spalding Family. Most of them are 50 years old and, in some cases, 75 years old.

Donated by Mrs. Margery Spalding, Elmtrees, Rainsford Road, Chelmsford; January, 1962.

Tumblers: i.e., toys with rounded bases that cannot fall over. All three made of papier mâché.

(*a*) Tumbler in the shape of Punch. Blue base, green and pink body with gold decoration, 12″ high.

(*b*) Miniature tumbler in the shape of a friar. Painted grey, 3½″ high.

(*c*) Miniature tumbler—painted yellow—face and hands painted on. 3½″ high.

Two sets of miniature wooden soldiers standing on "Trellis work" enabling their ranks to be opened and closed. 1½″ high.

(*a*) 13 sailors with arms outstretched.

(*b*) 13 Guards soldiers, with rifles at the slope, led by a drummer.

Wooden clown, dressed in purple and red quartered costume—yellow painted face and red painted hat, 8½″ high, with moving arms and legs. Made in Germany.

Clockwork London omnibus of C1920. Open top type. Painted red. Mechanism broken. Made in Germany; 8″ long, 5″ high.

Two peg dolls with wooden painted heads, one white, one block and string arms. 6½″ high. Dressed in white cotton nightdresses.

Wooden toy—"Shoot the Chute"—consisting of a wooden open truck and an inclined ramp. 3½′ long. Made in Germany.

Victorian wax doll, 1' 6" high, wearing elaborate rose-coloured ball dress, trimmed with white lace, blonde hair braided and in ringlets. Wearing earrings and necklace.

Mechanical clown, 1' 9" high, seated on wooden chair. When wound up, plays the violin, at the same time turning his head from side to side, rolling his eyes, and poking out his tongue.

COLCHESTER AND ESSEX MUSEUM
THE CASTLE, COLCHESTER, ESSEX.

Open: *Weekdays, 10—5.*
   Sunday, 2.30—5 during period April—October only.
   Also HOLLY TREES MANSION.

Open: *Weekdays, 10—1; 2—5.*

Admission Free to both Museums.

Collection of Clay Figurines

Many toy historians not over-punctilious about their terms of reference, have described as "toys of baked clay" these tomb-figures, all dating from Roman graves of children, excavated in the Colchester region. They may be excused for the error in that this description appeared on official picture postcards in the Colchester Corporation's own Museum Series published (with the town's coat-of-arms) in 1952.

At variance in opinion with British Museum authorities, the Curator asks for these to be described here as Clay Figurines, but that they "were used as toys is acceptable".

Those on exhibition were all found in a single grave. They were accompanied by coins and glass vessels of glass, pottery and bronze, which date the grave from about 50 A.D. and comprise: —

Hercules, with club and lion's skin.

Figure of a clown (?); the hands are pierced so that the figure could probably be made to climb up a double string.

Five caricatures of an old man reading from a scroll. Conjectured to represent the schoolmaster; but also suggested it might be a reciter.

Four togate, reclining figures (the Romans lay in this manner at table).

Figure of a bull, with three horns. (A Celtic deity.)

Young male head for a doll.

The several small pottery phials (for ointment) in form of goat, hare (three), lion (two), pig and monkey (three) are hardly genuine toys.

COLCHESTER also has a large collections of Toys in the Holly Trees Mansion.

DARTFORD BOROUGH MUSEUM
MARKET STREET, DARTFORD, KENT.

Open: Weekdays (except Wednesday), 2.30—5.30. Admission Free.

Objects Connected with Childhood

Edison-Bell Picturegram with picture spools and disc records by Harry Hemsley. This is simply an acoustic gramophone playing small electrically recorded discs consisting of a commentary or narrative while a coloured continuous paper strip depicting a well-known fairy story or other children's tale unrolls from one vertical roller, across a proscenium, to another roller. Synchronisation is effected by a belt drive from the gramophone turntable to the roller system. These machines cost 6 guineas when new and only remained on the market for two or three years, probably due to their high price and the economic depression beginning in 1929. There are probably few surviving examples. It was apparently placed on the market as a children's version of the then new development of Talking Pictures in the cinemas.

Children's disc records (including nursery rhymes), all 7″ electrical recordings of C1929.

Philips' scale of areas of squares and their equivalent square roots, consisting of a short strip of thin wood with attached paper scale. Late Victorian/Edwardian.

Children's hand coloured lantern slides, including extracts from "Beauty and the Beast" and "The Sleeping Beauty", C1860, and some similar ones with lever movement (e.g., to produce rolling of ship in ocean, or movement of horse's head) made in Germany, C1900.

Two stereoscopes, C1895 and 1902, and stereoscopic photographs from 1889-1902. These were also used by adults but many of the photographs are of Cherry Kearton's natural history subjects, no doubt chiefly intended for young people.

A small series of children's clothes (caps, smocks, etc., used for nursery purposes), 1785—end of 19th century.

Victorian doll's gloves.

Wooden kaleidoscope, C1900.

Children's cheap paper books, with lithographed illustrations: —
- (*a*) "The Battle of Chevy Chase", C1835.
- (*b*) Pictures of the Great Exhibition, London, 1851, unfolding to form three-dimensional models, C1855.

Laminated bone domino. Victorian.

Greetings card to a child. Victorian.

A small unpainted wooden toy cow. C18th-early 19th century. This was found when the Monastery behind Longfield Church, near Dartford, was being demolished.

A home-made zoëtrope (early 19th century) with a collection of paper strips and card discs C1850 labelled "Clarke's Wheel of Fortune" and "Clarke's Zoëtrope". The maker, Mr. Clarke, had premises in Garrick Street (London ?).

DERBY MUSEUM AND ART GALLERY
WARDWICK, DERBY.
Open: Weekdays, 10—6.
Sundays, 2.30—4.30.
Admission Free.

The Museum possesses a large collection of dolls, toys and games of the 18th and 19th centuries, of which the following is a summary: —

Large Toys

Baby's wooden cradle; rocking horse; pushcart, drawn by two prancing horses, C1870; doll's perambulator, C1910. All English.

Dolls, Dolls' Clothing, etc.

Over 20 dolls of wax, china, wax/composition, china/ composition, and rag, mainly English, with one or two French and German examples, dating 1800-1900, all dressed, together with a selection of separate garments, of which the most unusual is a pair of doll's leather boots, from Canada, 19th century. There is also a doll's Staffordshire china tea service, C1920.

Various Toys and Games

English carved ivory cup-and-ball, 18th century; Peepshow "View of the Thames Tunnel", 1825; Lead toys (20), representing market scene, French, C1850; "English Cuirassiers", being 12 lead soldiers, Nuremberg, C1840; "The Castle of the Commander-in-Chief", a military game of 52 pieces (fort, soldiers, cannon), in original box, German, C1840; "The Cousin and the Aunt", bowing heads with hair, hats, etc., French, C1840; "Jeu des Mosaiques Humaines", original box containing incomplete set of dissected features from which players built up complete faces, French, C1840; two Noah's Arks, ? English, C1870; "Trailers", forming part of a Circus procession, ? English, C1880; ABC animal bricks in original box, American, 1885; "Snapdragon", a miniature hoopla game, ? English, C1900.

Board and Dice Games

"New Game of Emulation", London, 1804; Panorama of Europe", a finely engraved and coloured sheet mounted on linen, with original case and player's instructions, London, 1816; "Survey of London", London, C1800; "Mother Goose", engraved and coloured sheet, with rules printed below, London, C1810; "The Journey", linen-backed coloured sheet, with spinner card (not original), London, C1848; "The Cottage of Content", London, C1848; "Bobs, the Great War Game", coloured board with counters and dice in box. Based on events of the Boer War, English, C1910.

Card Games

"The Wandering Jew", 16 cards, German, 1832; "Hide and Seek with the Kings and Queens of England", Series II, 84 cards, London, C1880; "Peter Puzzlewigs Mirthful Game of Alliteration", 26 cards, London, C1840; "The Infant's Poetical Cabinet", 12 cards, London, C1860; "Historical Lotto", 12 cards with 204 matching dated cards, German, C1890; Incomplete pack of playing cards, Gibson Hunt, London, 1773; Pack printed by Thomas Creswick, with 16 bone fish-shaped counters, and miniature copy of "Hoyle's Games", English, 18th century; Incomplete pack of "Old Maid" cards, English, C1900.

Jig-saw and Dissected Puzzles

"Life of Jesus", C1820; "Royal Chronological Tables of English History", Wallis, London, 1788; "Making China", Wallis, London, 1810; "Life of a Farmer", C1840; "The Dockyard and the Ship in all its Stages", with informative booklet, C1840; "Animals in Action", Wallis, London, C1790; "Betty Foy and Her Idiot Boy", the text of Wordsworth's poem, and picture, Ogilvy, London, 1840; Dissected puzzle of 36 cubes, making six pictures, C1890.

Books

"The Youngster's Diary", Davison, Alnwick, *circa* 1790; "Enigmes Chinoises" Toy Book (figures and architecture for colouring, cutting out and mounting on wood), French, *circa* 1800; "The Life of Jack Spratt" (Chap Book), Rusher, Banbury, *circa* 1810; "The House that Jack Built", Gibb, Glasgow, *circa* 1840; Five chap books (Houlston, London, 1846-47), by Mrs. Cameron: "The Little Dog Flora", "The Nosegay of Honeysuckle", "The Warning Clock"; by Mrs. Sherwood: "The History of Emily and Her Brothers", "A Mother's Duty"; "The Toy Book Present " (coloured engravings with verse letterpress), Religious Tract Society, *circa* 1870.

HEREFORD CITY MUSEUM
BROAD STREET, HEREFORD.
Open: *Weekdays, 10—6.30 (10—5 on Thursdays).*
Sunday, 2—5.30.
Admission Free.

The collection of toys, although not large, contains some good examples of board and card games; dolls' furniture; and a considerable number of dolls dating from the early 19th to the early 20th centuries.

This material, while it is not spectacular, would be worth a visit from anyone seriously studying toys.

HOVE MUSEUM OF ART
19 NEW CHURCH ROAD, HOVE, SUSSEX.
Closed Good Friday, Christmas Day and Boxing Day.
Open: *Mondays to Saturdays, 10—1, 2—5.*
Sundays, 2.30—5.
Admission Free.

The Museum has a growing collection of children's toys and dolls, the greater part of which is stored, but is available for research to teachers, collectors or students.

The Doll's Room

This contains four dolls' houses: —

   (i) The Hansard House, of three storeys, made by H. L. Hansard, 1912.

   (ii) A small four-roomed house, furnished in Edwardian period style.

   (iii) A larger five-roomed house, also in Edwardian style, lent by Mrs. G. A. V. Connelly, of Brighton.

   (iv) A painted wood house of six rooms, with dolls and furniture of 1850, the gift of Miss Veasey.

Dolls and Dolls' Clothes

There are two showcases of dolls, the earliest of which dates from 1708, and a varied collection of clothes, mainly of the 19th century.

Toys and Games

Again, a large and varied collection, ranging from a 40-gun wooden battleship, fire engines and a traction engine from the late 19th century, to the Coronation Coach of 1953. Board games include "Toad in the Hole" of 1780 and "The Reward of Merit", 1801.

CLIFFE CASTLE MUSEUM
KEIGHLEY, Nr. BRADFORD, YORKS.

Administered by the Borough of Keighley Art Gallery and Museum Department, all specimens in this growing collection are numbered and classified. Some indication of its range and scope is indicated by the following list: —

Dolls, etc.

Wood Doll, arms painted and varnished.

Victorian Doll with extra clothing.

Early Victorian, hollow wax, handmade and hand-worked clothes.

Victorian Doll, plaster and wood, height 18″.

Doll and Wardrobe of clothes (Victorian), china head and limbs (complete with trunk to pack clothes in).

Two small dolls, 4½″, head and arms of pot.

Victorian Doll, early type, glass eyes. Height 17″.

Victorian Doll, height 2à″. Period 1874.

Doll, double headed. Late 19th century.

Wooden Doll - Pedlar Man. Wooden Doll - Pedlar Woman.

Victorian Doll, hair in ringlets, dressed frilled crinoline. Height 17″ (1874).

Victorian Dancing Doll, height 11½″. Wood, from first London Exhibition, 1851.

Dressed Doll in Case (Crinoline).

Eastern Doll, veiled.

Five 18th century Dolls in case.

Victorian Doll, bustle dress, C1880, wax face. Ditto, C1870.

Early Victorian Doll. Height 18″. Velvet dress with train.

Burmese Dolls.

Old Doll, not fully dressed, carved wood.

Two home-made Golliwogs, 21″, stuffed cloth.

French Costume Doll, modern Paris made (1940).

Doll with bustle dress, C1870.

Musical Box with five small Dolls (playing instruments).

Doll, C1885. Plaster limbs, china head, glass eyes.

Doll's Carriage, late Victorian, prob. 1865, basketwork.

Toy Coal Scuttle.

Doll's House, complete with furniture, late 19th century, from Craven family.

Doll's Bed, spring mattress. Late 19th or early 20th century.

Doll's Armchair—modern.

Doll's Kitchen with oddments in Teasets, etc.

Doll's Dinner Service (incomplete); Teaset—Davenport.

Porcelain (Chinese): Doll's Teaware; Teaset, miniature (Victorian), *papier mâché*. Tea Service, coloured flower design. Pottery Teaset (incomplete).

PLATE I

Pedlar Doll & Booth, Bethnal Green Museum. (See p. 17)

PLATE II

German Clockwork Train, c.1840, Victoria & Albert Museum. (See p. 16)

PLATE III

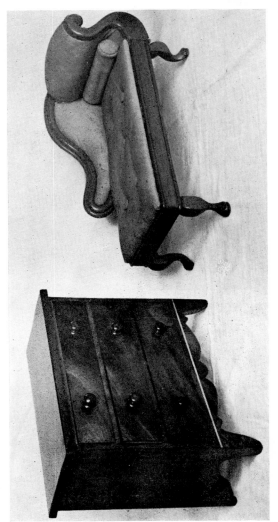

Queen Mary's Dolls' House Furniture, London Museum. (See p. 9)

PLATE IV
19th Century Dolls' Furniture, Cambridge Folk Museum. (See p. 27)

PLATE V
Toys at the City Museum, Leeds. (See p. 44)

PLATE VIII

More of the Toy Museum, Rottingdean. (See pp. 23-26)

[B.T.H.A. Photos]

PLATE IX

PLATE XII
Toy Horse & Railway Horsebox, Blithfield Hall (See pp. 51-53)

PLATE XIII

Victorian See-saw at Blithfield Hall

Doll's Clothing, Gloves, Stockings.

Doll's Furniture, Doll's Pram (C1915). Eastern Doll with Yashmak.

Three foreign Dolls (modern): American Indian, Moorish, Madeira.

Miniature Wooden Dolls in small Book Box.

Three Dolls made of wire and dressed (servant, mistress and master).

Victorian Dolls (two).

Five Dutch Dolls (wooden). Two dressed Victorian: *see* Pollocks guide.

Doll with padded skirt for use as pincushion.

Period Doll 90 years old.

"Lady Isobel" eyes operate by lever inside body (1867).

Walking Doll (autoperipathikos).

Welsh Costume Doll.

Victorian Doll, wax head.

Doll (C1850-60).

Porcelain Doll, 1850-60.

Two Dolls (1860s and 1870s).

Doll, mauve period dress (Victorian).

Two Small Dolls, dressed period.

Victorian Doll, C1880.

Large ditto.

Victorian doll dressed in blue velvet.

Games and Toys

"Fun, Wit and Humour"—games board.

Building Bricks (incomplete set in box).

Toy Aeroplane.

Child's Jig-saw.

Rattle—silver mountings.

"The Reward of Merit" variation of "Game of Goose".

Glove Puppet.

Diabolo.

"Middleton's Game of England and Wales" with counters.

Child's Toy Steam Engine.

Fowl made from *papier mâché,* formerly contained small Easter Eggs.

Football Cards (collections), "Snap" Cards (Victorian).

Model Plough drawn by Bullocks.

Picture Alphabet.

Tumbling Acrobat.

Snake in Egg. Toy Menagerie.

Set of early Victorian Wooden Toys.

"Glassies" Glass Marbles.

Miniature Children's Plates (hand spinning), Sunday School Band of Hope Scene.

Toy Top Hat.

Bundle of Spillikins—made by Dr. Brigg.

Pack of Plain Cards with Scripture Texts, hand-written.

Game of Quartettes. Game in box—Schimmel or The Bell & Hammer.

"Lotto". "Checks".

Karden's Adventure of Robinson Crusoe.

"What you Buy" by Professor Punch.

Dissected Puzzles: "Crystal Palace"; Forty Birds from Ostrich to Humming Bird; "Sovereigns of England".

The Royal and Most Pleasant Game of Goose.

Egyptian Top (Pig made from soft stone).

Cut-out Paper Animals with Letters.

Japanese Acrobats: wooden shoes.

Magic Lantern.

Pollock Toy Theatre.

Transparencies. Child's Panorama.

Toy Sewing Machine.

Wood Cradle.

Iron Money Boxes (Caster Bank and Tower Bank).

Tin Money Box. "Jolly Nigger" Money Box.

Iron Money Box (six sections), 1882.

Spherical Cast Iron Money Boxes.

Mahogany chest-of-drawers Money Box.
Chinese Rice Figures on Sticks.

Outdoor Games
Child's Iron Hoop.
Clay "Taws".
"Checks".

Children's Books
A small collection.

ROYAL BOTANIC GARDENS, KEW
KEW, MIDDLESEX.

Opening Times for Houses & Museum: 1—4.50 (*Weekdays*).
1—5.50 (*Sundays*).

Admission, 3d.

Within the grounds of these world-famous botanical gardens is a Wood Museum. Known as Museum No. 3, it is located near the New Gate at the Kew Green end of the Gardens.

Here may be seen an absorbing exhibit of ring-cut toys from Saxony—the traditional hand-crafted range of Noah's Ark animals and birds made over the centuries in the Black Forest area of Germany, and revived since the end of World War II.

In a well-documented showcase is a display of those pine-wood discs with the rough-cut animal shape in the centre, which would eventually be finished by the addition of tails, trunks, and so forth, and finally painted. The mass-production methods involved were devised by the villagers of Saxony, where many peasant communities, cut off by winter snows, turned to toy-making as an occupation.

THE STROUD MUSEUM
LANSDOWN, GLOUCESTERSHIRE.
Open: Weekdays, 10.30—1 and 2—5.
Admission Free.

This Museum, which is administered by the Cowle Trust, concentrates on local material such as paintings, photographs

43

and records of houses, mills and other topographical subjects.

Agriculture, household utensils and local crafts are also well represented. The Museum has a better-than-average collection of period and other dolls. These are not yet classified but experts like Mrs. Nerea de Clifford (*see* Page 111), and Mrs. O. Hassall, of The Manor House, Wheatley, Oxon, have made detailed Notes, the former for Doll Club purposes, the latter in fieldwork for a forthcoming study on toys in relation to handicraft.

LEEDS CITY MUSEUMS
ABBEY HOUSE, KIRKSTALL, YORKSHIRE.
Admission Free.

This important collection was previously known as the Kirkstall Abbey House Collection of Toys and Games. A new gallery has been specially built to accommodate the items which in the past were not shown to advantage owing to lack of light and proper mounting.

The Museum occupies the former gatehouse of the old abbey, and attractive as its low rooms and leaded windows are, set in stone walls several feet thick, they held many problems for the Curator, Mr. C. M. Mitchell, when exhibits required space and light.

He has built up the nucleus during the past ten years so that it now comprises several thousand pieces, all card-indexed.

Owned, as a child, by the daughter of the former occupant of the old gatehouse (one of the four outsized Dolls' Houses dated 1850-1860)—was left in its old home, as a gift to the Museum, when the property was bought by Leeds Corporation. Another, 40 years older, is a ten-room country house. All are furnished with a completeness calculated to send any child into raptures—even down to the miniature sponges and tablets of soap lying on the mahogany tops of the Victorian baths, and the razors and strops hanging from the bathroom walls. The kitchens are equipped with a generous supply of tiny pots, pans, jacks, spits, jars of pickles, and plates of succulent-looking hams and chickens. The tiny coal-scuttle in the "drawing room" of the villa holds fragments of real coal, and on a table a minute syphon and whisky bottle await "papa's" pleasure. On another table is the inevitable Victorian family Bible, while on the wall of the bedroom above hangs the equally inevitable framed text.

Much of the furniture in the larger house is as rare as it is perfect. On the open flap of a miniature Chippendale-style bookcase-bureau is a tiny book, $\frac{1}{4}''$ x $\frac{1}{8}''$, published in 1838, printed in minute but legible type. Oak-panelled walls, delicately moulded doors, shell-encrusted sofas, cabinets filled with minute china offer miniature expressions of Victorian prosperity—even the tiny lap-dog on the hearth has a silk cushion to himself!

A product of the Stuart period, the oldest English doll in the collection, made of wood and nearly 2' tall, has an elaborate stumpwork contemporary costume, while a Victorian doll —which wears a mauve silk "creation" with a flowing train— possesses a "wardrobe" of no less than eight dresses, each with its own set of underwear and accessories. These are the aristocrats of the show-case reserved for dolls, but for companions they have dolls of all sizes, in every degree of shabbiness and stylishness.

Boys usually make for the case housing examples of the earliest toy trains; tops dating back to 1750; soldiers made between 100 and 150 years ago, and skittles and marbles of varying ages, or another case which shows the development of "moving pictures" in toy form. The toy theatre is an exhibit on its own, with "Penny Plain, Twopence Coloured" characters and settings—and scripts for fifteen plays. In mint condition, Mr. Mitchell discovered it in a pile of oddments at a sale.

Many of the pen and pencil games in the collection could serve as general knowledge or intelligence tests for children today.

War and battle tactics, which provided the original inspiration for games like chess and draughts have, more
recently, provided games of topical interest. Kirkstall has
several such games which enjoyed temporary popularity in
the First World War.

LUTON MUSEUM AND ART GALLERY
WARDOWN PARK, LUTON, BEDS.

Admission Free.

The Museum contains a representative selection of dolls,
toys, games, baby carriages, etc., but the most remarkable
items are a group of straw dolls dating from the 19th century,
made by the local straw plaiters. (Luton was formerly the
chief centre of this craft.)

MAIDSTONE MUSEUM AND ART GALLERY
FAITH STREET, MAIDSTONE, KENT.

Admission Free.

The Museum possesses a small collection of dolls, wooden,
wax and china, mainly as an adjunct to a good display of
period costume, principally of the 18th-20th centuries.

THE PINTO COLLECTION
OF WOODEN BYGONES
OXHEY WOODS HOUSE,
OXHEY DRIVE, Nr. NORTHWOOD., MIDDLESEX

Open: April—September: Wed., Thurs., Sat., Sun.,
Good Friday & Bank Holidays,
2—6.45.
Admission: 2/6d. Children, 1/-.
Terms for Parties.

*Some of the items in the Toy Section of the Pinto Collec-
tion:—*

Dolls

Doll, Schoenhut, American patent; Balancing Dolls; Dutch Dolls; Articulated wooden figures, including Peter Pan characters; Figures for a scene entitled "The Schoolroom" and many others.

Outdoor Games

Bilboquets (a cup and ball game) of many varieties; Tops of many varieties; Knur and spel; Tip cats; Yo-yo's; Diabolos.

Toys, Miscellaneous

Magic lantern and slides; Stereoscopes; Miniature furniture and other objects such as a model Halifax wicker-work horse-drawn tram; Puppets—Punch and Judy Show; Nesting toys; Noah's Ark; Spades (sand digging); Spillikins; Quoits; Set of nine-pins and ball in box dated 1796; Hobby horses; Jumping Jacks; Skipping Ropes; A jester's bauble; Toad-in-the-Hole; Horn-books, including a unique combined doll/rattle/horn-book; Child's corrective finger stocks; Deportment or back-board; a baby-trotter; a Cricket or Dame School clicker; Wallis's Revolving Alphabet; Alphabet bat and alphabet sticks; Many varieties of building blocks, including Crandall's building blocks; a late 17th century Polychrome painted, book and pencil satchel-box from Hinderloopen; a child's Georgian travelling mouse cage.

Miscellaneous Board and Table Games

Chess, draughts, dominoes, cribbage, backgammon, merrils, solitaire, Pope Joan, Fox & Geese, Lotto, Royal Game of Nines. Table croquet set and stand, Squails; Puzzles, such as inter-locking globes, barrels, etc.; Jig-saws, including early specimens, mostly educational; Tumbler toys; Bagatelle; a number of educational games, including Mentor cards, etc.

There are many other items not listed, but in the food preparation section are carved moulds for gingerbread horn-books, Punch and Judy and other fairy-tale characters, with casts taken from them alongside. Moulds for a child's clay pipe, for soldiers, for sugar mottoes, etc., are also displayed with their respective casts.

MUSEUM OF DOMESTIC LIFE
STRANGER'S HALL,
CHARING CROSS, NORWICH, NORFOLK.

Open: Weekdays, 10—1; 2—5.
Admission: Adults, 1/-; Children, 6d.; Tuesdays & Fridays only.
Other days, Free.

The Museum consists of 14 Period rooms, all exquisitely furnished and maintained, and an Exhibition Room of Toys ranging from the 17th to the 20th centuries. These include two late 18th century wooden dolls; two wooden chairmen, C1700, to carry a sedan chair; a "Queen Anne" 12" high with panniers and a wooden pedlar doll; a wax doll, "Queen of Hearts". There are also some charming examples of miniature furniture in the two fully-furnished and well-lit period Dolls' Houses.

Among the various children's games are a delightful Toy Theatre, the oldest single playing-card in England, and a very ornate "walking-chair".

One of the other attractions, especially to the doll-collector, is a Victorian night-nursery, with a particularly interesting group of wax dolls.

NOTTINGHAM CITY MUSEUM
AND ART GALLERY
THE CASTLE, NOTTINGHAM.

Open: April to September: Weekdays, 10—6.45.
(10—5.45 on Fridays)
Sunday, 2—4.45.
Open: October to March: Weekdays, 10—dusk.
Sunday, The three hours before dusk.
Admission Free.
1d. on Sunday; 3d. on Bank Holidays.

The Toy collection here has not yet been classified or indexed; the following incomplete list is added by courtesy of Mrs. O. Hassall, who has made notes for a forthcoming study.

Jig-saw Puzzle in the form of map, 1794; adaptation of "The Paths of Life".

Ping-pong Bat, 19th century.

Nine Pins, 19th century.

Shuttlecock with unusual cone-shaped catchers.

Cup and ball and yo-yo, 19th century; diabolos of bone, brass and rubber.

Skipping rope with fine wooden handles.

Toy horse, 17th century (rider lost), found under old Livery Yard at the "Black Boy" Hotel, operated by crankshaft to give cantering action.

Japanese "Empress" Doll, 1868.

Chinese rattle of carved ivory.

North American Indian pottery figures of animals, turtles, etc., ranging from Arizona to New Mexico.

Basement

Noah's Ark.

Dolls, 1835-1840.

Wax and China Dolls, 1850-1870.

Wooden Dolls, undated.

Dolls' Costumes and Clothes.

Baby Doll.

THE PITT-RIVERS MUSEUM
PARKS ROAD, OXFORD.

Open: *Weekdays, for Students only, 9—5.*
Weekdays, for General Public, 2—4; or by Written Appointment.

Admission Free.

The Museum is concerned primarily with Ethnology and Pre-history, with special reference as to the origin, development and geographical distribution of arts and industries not requiring elaborate machinery.

Toys and playthings of ethnographic interest consist largely of playdolls, votive dolls and figurines and magico-religious variants. A representative idea of the range and scope of these is given by the following: —

Africa

Mohammedan doll from Mombasa, Kenya, bamboo, 8".

Dolls from the Sudan made from cane and clay; stuffed arms.

Omdurman Dervish rag-dolls, 18".

Coptic doll from Illahun, wooden, $5\frac{1}{2}$".

Kaffir doll made of strong leather, coloured red, possibly representing a Hottentot, $14\frac{1}{2}$".

Arctic Region

Eskimo man, wood, dressed in furs.

North America

Doll of the Tewa Indians, Arizona, $5\frac{1}{2}$".

South America

Ancient clay doll from Peru, 6".

Doll from New Mexico, leather and horsehair, 12".

Wooden doll from Jacya (rare specimen).

Man and woman dolls, made from palm leaves, Costa Rica.

Clown from New Mexico in pink terracota, 10".

Fertility dolls, terracotta, from Brazil, wearing raffia skirts, 4".

Madagascar

Doll from Sakalava tribe made from cloth. Brown face and black hair, carrying baby on her back wrapped in white linen, $8\frac{1}{2}$"

(See also MUSICAL BOXES, *page* 173).

PETERBOROUGH MUSEUM
AND ART GALLERY
PRIESTGATE, PETERBOROUGH, NORTHANTS.

Admission Free.

While the City Museum contains no large or important collection of juvenilia, enthusiasts in the vicinity might find a visit rewarding.

MUSEUM OF CHILDHOOD & COSTUME
BLITHFIELD HALL, Nr. RUGELEY, STAFFS.

Opening Times: *Weds., Thurs., Sats. & Suns., 2.30—6, Easter to October.*

Also Bank Holiday Mondays, 12—7.

Tuesdays after Bank Holidays, 2.30—6.

Admission: *Adults, 2/6; Children, 1/6.*

Car Park: *Cars, 6d.; Motor Cycles, 3d.; Coaches, Free.*

Since 1086, Blithfield Hall has been the home of the de Blithfield family and their descendants, the Bagots, the present owner being Nancy, Lady Bagot. The Hall contains, among other things, a unique collection of Stuart relics and Georgian costume, and, of course, the famous Museum of Childhood, in which some of the many exhibits are as follows: —

The Doll's House is a model of a house built in Adelaide, S. Australia, 1896. Period furniture.

The Baby Rocker was found in the stables and may have been made by the Estate Carpenter for the Bagot children, in which case it would probably be over 100 years old.

The Rocking Horse and Horse Box, also bought from a London antique dealer, thought to be one carriage from a complete train.

Sleigh. Made in Holland, 1763. Bagot arms painted on the back. Found in a London antique shop six years ago.

See-saw. Victorian, with two small chairs for the children to sit in.

Rocking Horses: One Regency, one Victorian (for two riders).

Baby Carriage: C1790. Lent by the National Trust from the Snowshill Collection.

Regency Baby Carriage: Carved wood in the shape of a shell.

Victorian Baby Carriage.

Furniture

Two high chairs.

One folding chair with cane back and seat.

Nursery screen. Hip bath and wash stand.

Glass-fronted bookcase.

One cradle, carved mahogany; one Hepplewhite cradle.

Child's four-poster bed.

Iron bedstead and similar bedstead for doll.

Desk and chair. Wing armchair.

Costumes

Page boy's costume made C1830.

Girl's dress, C1830.

Several christening robes and baby's bonnets.

Toys

Dolls' house furniture, several dolls' perambulators; high chairs and sofa. Doll's trunk.

Pedlar doll. Four wax-faced dolls.

Dolls in National costume (several lent by the National Trust).

Victorian travelling Punch and Judy puppets.

Two booths or "bazaars" with saleswomen.

Several china tea and dinner services, and one green glaze dessert service.

Musical Boxes. "The Dancing Dolls", made in the shape of a dance floor, which vibrates slightly, making the carved and painted dolls, mounted on bristles, "dance".

Barrel organ, with monkey.

Hand painted card games for teaching French.

Miniature draughts and roulette.

Decalcomania, or "the art of transferring coloured drawings to wood, china and other works of art".

New and interesting German game of "Prisma". (?)

Noah's Ark, animals of painted wood.

Model of Pickfords' horse-drawn dray. Model coaches.

Ponyskin covered toy horse on wheels.

Model of Victorian railway carriage with loose box and horse.

Painted glass slides from Magic Lantern.

Several games of Solitaire and Spillikins.

Educational Cards

    The Infants' Cabinet of birds, fishes, insects, flowers, Les
      Cris de Paris.

Books

    Pictures of English History in Miniature, designed by
      Alfred Mills; 1824.

    The Death and Burial of Cock Robin.

    The Cries of London, 1805.

    The History of Little Fanny, 1810.

    The Maids of Lee.

    The Men of Ware.

    Come Lasses and Lads (illustrated by R. Caldecott).

    Sing a Song of Sixpence.

    John Gilpin.

    Daddy Darwin's Dovecote (R. Caldecott).

    A painting book by Kate Greenaway.

    The Infants' Library.

    The Yellow Shoe Strings, 1821.

    William's Secret, 1819.

    Henry, 1817.

    Peggy and Her Mammy, 1819.

    Baby Tales, 1813.

    Select Fables of Aesop.

    Alfred Bagot's Eton Journal, 1830.

    Letter written by Henrietta Bagot (aged seven) to her
      brother William, February 24th, 1787.

ST. IVES, CORNWALL

A collection of approximately 1,000 optical toys, early
cameras, cinema projectors and other historical items of a
like nature, the property of John and William Barnes, is
understood to be on exhibition at St. Ives, but precise details
were not available at the time of going to press.

THE NATIONAL TRUST
SNOWSHILL, GLOUCESTERSHIRE.

*Open on Saturdays in April and from May to mid-October on
Wednesdays, Thursdays and Saturdays, 2—6.
Sundays and Bank Holidays, 11—1 and 2—6.*

Admission 2/6. Children, 1/3.

*Parties of 20, 1/6 each. Parties only by arrangement
with the Curator (Broadway 2110).*

THE NATIONAL TRUST is a society founded in 1895 by Miss
Octavia Hill, Sir Robert Hunter and Canon Rawnsley. It
exists to preserve places of natural beauty or historic interest
for everyone to enjoy. Although incorporated by special Act
of Parliament in 1907, it is not financed by the State.

Its work hitherto has been made possible by many individual donors of property; by friends who have responded to a
succession of public appeals; and by others who have sub-
scribed annually to its general funds. Its work in the future
can only be carried on if this generous support is steadily
increased.

Many of the Country Houses and other properties administered by the National Trust maintain in their furnished
rooms individual or groups of children's playthings—ranging
from Rocking Horses to Dolls and Dolls' Houses. Where these
are located may be found out by enquiring from the Secretary,
National Trust, 42 Queen Anne's Gate, London, S.W.1.

The most interesting is, perhaps, Snowshill Manor, where
its late owner assembled a most fascinating collection of the
curious and the antique from all countries and representing
many exotic cultures. The rooms are all named picturesquely
and the juvenile interest lies in a room known as "Seventh
Heaven", situated on the left of the old stairs.

There is a fully descriptive booklet on sale at the Manor.

Toys and Models in "Seventh Heaven" include the following: —

Two dolls' houses, early 19th century.

Wind toys—a man in beaver hat and a soldier—the arms revolve in the wind.

Italian marionette or puppet—a man in armour.

A series of dolls, dolls' beds and furniture.

Model train in wood, C1850—engine, tender, 1st, 2nd and 3rd class coaches, the latter open, seat for guard on the top of closed coach, lettered N. & Y.R.

Model pantechnicon with pair of dapple grey horses.

Toy theatre, by Benjamin Pollock, Hoxton, with several sets of scenery.

Model Broughams and other carriages.

Model of South African covered wagon.

Two "baby-walkers", one attached to a post, the other in a frame on legs.

Model of the "Magnet" stage coach, 1840, made by H.R. (?) Waiting, 1936.

TORQUAY NATURAL HISTORY SOCIETY MUSEUM
BABBACOMBE ROAD, TORQUAY, DEVON.

Open: Weekdays, 10—5.

Admission, 1/-. Children, 6d.

An attractively displayed Children's Corner in the Museum contains, among other objects: —

A Doll's House, large, with a good representative collection of furniture of early 19th century.

A Noah's Ark, large, with over 100 animals, some of rather unusual type.

Children's Books.

Dolls, some of an early date.

ROYAL TUNBRIDGE WELLS MUSEUM
AND ART GALLERY
CIVIC CENTRE, TUNBRIDGE WELLS, KENT.

Open: Weekdays, 10—5.30. (Closed on Bank Holidays.)

Admission Free.

This Museum has a large collection of toys, games and dolls, together with dozens of dolls' accessories.

There are 119 dolls at the time of writing, excluding doll's house figures—two very fine dolls' houses, fully furnished; several shops—a milliner's (quite unique), butcher's and greengrocer's.

A small collection of Victorian toys, including a zoëtrope.

Panoramas, and an early Pollock Theatre with the original sets and script.

One case is devoted to Georgian and Victorian table games. Also on view is a large collection of model soldiers.

The Museum has inherited from local families the gifts of three old collections of toys. These are catalogued under the names of the donors:—

The Breton Collection.

The Fynmore Collection.

The Weekes Collection.

WARWICK COUNTY MUSEUM
MARKET PLACE, WARWICK.

Open: Mon., Tues., Wed., Thurs. & Sat, 10—12.30.

1.30—5.30.

Sunday, May—September, 2.30—5.

Closed Friday.

Admission Free.

A miscellaneous collection of playthings contains the following items:—

About a dozen dolls—wooden, wax and china.

About a dozen dissected puzzles of the 19th century.

About half a dozen educational games.

Some 15 children's picture books and riddles, including most of the books illustrated by Randolph Caldecott.

Marbles, blood alleys and a "cobber".

Set of quoits and one bronze quoit.

A tip-cat (modern).

Tops (4) and shuttlecocks (2).

Cup and ball (1), 19th century.

Two sets of bezique.

Two sets of dominoes.

One set of chess, four sets of playing cards and three sets of ivory game counters.

Noah's Ark and animals.

Toy village and toy railway train, C1830.

John Gilpin and his horse.

Four sets of bricks.

19th century toy engine.

WORTHING MUSEUM AND ART GALLERY
CHAPEL ROAD, WORTHING, SUSSEX.

Opening Times: *Weekdays, 10—8.*

10—5 (*October to March*).

The Guermonpres Collection of Toys comprises:—

1. Large collection of dolls dating from 1820, including three jointed wooden dolls of this period, dressed.

   A Fairy Doll of 1830-40.

   A baby doll with a straw body and a long, handmade robe of 1860.

   Several dolls with wax faces and arms and cloth bodies one dated 1830.

A boy doll in cadet uniform, probably French, 1850.
Three mechanical dolls of 1880.
A doll with jointed limbs, open and shut eyes, 1880.
Several porcelain dolls, about 1880-90.
A pair of dolls in Greek costume.
A Negro doll and a doll with a ping-pong ball head
of 1920.
Quantity of dolls' clothes of all periods.

2. Large Regency Doll's House and a quantity of doll's house furniture, including an upright piano, upholstered settees and chairs, table and cupboards, mirrors and lamps, a coal scuttle with imitation coal, fire irons including bellows, a cradle and beds with bedding and a doll, a desk with a leather top, a tapestry work carpet, a gong, three clocks and many kitchen utensils.

3. A magic lantern with slides, some alphabet letters. A kaleidoscope. A cardboard camera with glass lens. A crystal ball with answers on a sheet of paper. A table tennis set. A miniature croquet set. A circular target and three spring loaded toy guns. Miniature shuttles. A tin drum and tambourine, C1900. Three penny whistles, 1850. Tin trumpet. Glockenspiel of six bells on a stand. Three bus conductor sets. A metal construction kit and a fretsaw set with patterns and tools. A toy shop with scales, etc., 1910. A farm of 300 animals, and model villages, dating back to 1850. Building blocks dating from 1835, including a set called "Solving the Dreadnought Question, 1911".

4. Of 30 packs of playing cards one is dated 1799, called "The Geography of England and Wales" and includes directions and a map in a case. There is a hand painted set dated 1810, as well as "Happy Families" and "Snap", a game called "Doctor Bushy" dated 1840, "Characters from Dickens", 1880, and "Panko", 1914.

The usual games of Draughts, Ludo, Halma and Lotto are included in this collection. There are spinning tops, bubblepipes and indoor fireworks, as well as magic novelties, including "The Disappearing Handkerchief Trick", "The Suspense Matchbox" and the "Magic Nail".

5. The large collection of clockwork toys, mostly dated 1900-1920 include a tiller steered car of 1903 and a submarine of the 1914 era. There are clockwork and tracked railway engines, rolling stock and accessories including a footbridge, signals, a warning bell tower and destination boards.

Lead toys include a cannon with spring activated firing pin, soldiers, miniature French cavalry dated 1850, a tank dated 1916, 300 domestic animals and garden accessories with flowers and a gardener.

There are two wooden castles, one in two tiers which fold. Painted wooden foot and horse soldiers dated 1830-40. Two glove puppets and a string puppet and several animal and bird novelties such as, a duck with waving wings and a biting dog with a wagging tail complete this remarkable collection of toys covering a period of 150 years.

YORK CASTLE MUSEUM
TOWER STREET, YORK.

Open: Weekdays, 9.30—5.30 (9.30—4.30 October to March).
Sunday, 2—4.30.
Admission, 1/-; Children, 6d., to each building.
Admission, 1/6; Children, 9d., to both buildings.

One of the most representative Collections in the North of England of toys, games and other children's belongings—all splendidly mounted—are permanently on view at this Folk Museum of Yorkshire life.

Many groups are shown in a workshop or small retail shop in a unique presentation of "The Street of Shops" devised by the Collection's Founder, the late Dr. J. L. Kirk of Pickering, who methodically collected Bygones.

Unfortunately, no catalogue or Guide is available, nor even pictorial records of the exhibits, but it is hoped that these will soon exist to do justice to such an important collection.

Viewing "The Street of Shops" is to experience the illusion of slipping back into the tranquileity of a bygone age, remote from bustle. The facades and shop fronts are genuine remains salvaged from old York buildings and other sources. The fidelity of detail achieved in this reproduction has created an atmosphere so convincing that the old cobbled "Street" has a compelling charm and universal appeal.

Here in the rows of stores, craftshops—and even a Post Office and Victorian pub.—stands the shopwindow of Mr. Toyman. In its nostalgic setting the window-space is crammed with a mixed assortment of old toys such as might have been the stock of any traditional English toyshop sixty years ago, against the panes of which many a youngster pressed his, or her, nose.

Among the items selected for the window-display are: —
Parlour Aunt Sally; American, 19th century.
Wooden soldiers; early 19th century.
Wood block soldiers; early 19th century.
Working sand-toy of fiddler moving hand and leg; late 18th century.
Chinese doll, Chinese cup-and-ball in cotton thread.
Early wooden skittles.
Two American cast iron toys—bucking donkey and shooting money box; 19th century.
John Gilpin—wooden articulated figures of gentleman and rider; early 19th century.
Steam-powered traction engine; 19th century.
Crandall's Building Blocks—the acrobats; 1867.
Early turned wood yo-yo; oriental.
German-made Chinese-type balancers, mercury-operated; 19th century.
German clockwork walking soldier; early 20th century.
Straw-work Noah's Ark and unpainted wood animals.

Cast-iron locomotive, tender and truck, Wallwork's patent.

On the opposite side of Mr. Toyman's premises, a few paces further along, a selection of larger toys are shown on ground level behind plate-glass. These include: —

Tudor-style doll's house of 1890 containing nine rooms, hall and staircase, all fully furnished and peopled.

Toy street piano; 19th century.

Toy hay-wain with wooden horse on wheels; 19th century.

Doubled-ended pram of varnished wood; 19th century.

Large rocking horse, dappled grey; 19th century.

Horse tricycle; early 19th century.

Noah's Ark, painted animals.

Travelling menagerie with wooden animals; 19th century.

Three-wheeled push-chair, cast iron wheels; early 19th century.

To inspect the major part of the Kirk Collection of Toys, however, one needs to move out of the Castle Museum building, cross the circular lawn and enter the adjacent building, formerly The Debtors' Prison of York and still known by this name although incorporated into the City's Museum scheme. Here, upstairs in a well-lit gallery, and in "buttress"-shape wall cases that permit viewing from two sides, the following items are grouped. A welcome feature of the corridor is that one may move up one side and return along the opposite side without the least sense of being enclosed: —

1. Doll's house furniture and accessories (about 200 pieces).
2. Group of wax playdolls.
3. Punch and Judy booth (collapsible, about 3' x 3½') with a complete set of puppet characters (glove-operated), including several duplicates, e.g., policeman, etc.
4. Noah's Ark, with several sets of whitewood animals.
5. Carved animals and wooden figures, Central European.
6. Lead soldiers, a small proportion of the total collection.
7. Dolls' tea-sets and chinaware.

8. Two Georgian and Restoration character dolls, and four period dresses.

9. Furnished Victorian parlour and three playdolls.

10. Automata: The Dolls' Tea Party (musical-box); fortune-telling doll; three walking dolls; head-moving tiger; china doll (French) mounted on a white shaggy collie-dog which is possibly a stuffed guinea-pig.

11. Toy theatres and play sheets.

12. Two showcases devoted to table-games and board-games containing early example of "Goose"; instructional toys; playing cards for children; jig-saws; games that teach; puzzles; etc.

13. Toys of movement, including very early toy train operated by string-and-turn-bottle; unusual wind-toy; motorcar; locomotives; etc.

14. Heslington Hall Baby House (C1690-1700), believed to be the oldest specimen in Britain, complete with playdolls having carved wax faces, and scale furniture.

SCOTLAND

MUSEUM OF CHILDHOOD
HYNDFORD'S CLOSE, 34 HIGH STREET
(Opp. JOHN KNOX'S HOUSE), EDINBURGH.

Open: Weekdays, 10—5.
Admission, 6d.; Children, 3d.

Edinburgh Corporation's Museum of Childhood, primarily the achievement of Mr. Patrick Murray (who is now its Curator), is not a children's museum, but a museum about them. Based on the theory of the Folk Museum, it covers, historically, every aspect of the British child from babyhood to twelve years old. Although children frequent it, its intended appeal is to the adult, and its approach to them is gay, colourful and sophisticated. For the older generation it is intensely nostalgic. Fundamentally, its purpose is to preserve the all-too-easily lost things of childhood, and, while allowing them to offer their own sensitive appeal to the visitor, to make them at the same time the subject of close study. Each exhibit is treated systematically, and its date, history, country of origin and relationship to the adult world are developed as fully as knowledge permits. Begun in 1952 in a corner of an existing museum, it now has its own establishment in Edinburgh's Royal Mile. It has four floors devoted respectively to playthings, hobbies and occupations, costumes and upbringing, and reading and education. Under playthings are dolls, all the toys, soldiers, tops and marbles, puzzles, bricks, cards and every variety of board-games, and the like. Hobbies and occupations include the incredible skills of bygone childhood: Potichomania,* Persian, Poonah and

---

* The art of applying scraps and other cut-out pictures to the inside of glass vessels.

letter painting, feather, seaweed, shell and hairwork, sand pictures and all the pins, needles and scraps of forgotten stuffs, materials and colours which surrounded children's activities in the past. Costume and upbringing deal with everything from Christening gowns to Dreadnought suits, and include such trifles as jewellery, dancing-class fans, mittens and wrist warmers, and such trials as back-boards. It glances at sweets, chocolate and biscuit boxes, but counters heavily with a vintage castor oil ('99; a fine, full-bodied year, with a distinct crust), Doctor Gregory's Powder, brimstone and treacle and "Black Jack" among other horrors. The last floor deals with every kind of book. Picture and story book, pop-ups, "Protean figures", classics and forgotten classics from the Butterfly's Ball onwards, all the forgotten writers and the near forgotten: the Gilsons, Breretons, May Baldwins, and Dorothy L. Moores of a happier age. There is a magnificent collection of Bloods, Jack Harkaways, Dick Turpins, Buffalo Bills, Robin Hoods, Greyfriars, Dixon Hawkes and Sexton Blakes, and such others as Lot-o'-Fun, Rainbow, Tiger Tim and Comic Cuts. An almost equally large collection is of school books, from Cocker, of the "According to", to such masters as North and Hillard, and Lady Bell, famous for "French Without Tears".

The toy collection is classified wherever possible, either by material or function; i.e., wooden, metal, paper and "plastic" or "soft", "construction", "optical", etc., toys. In describing an exhibit every effort is made to give date and country of origin, and to develop its background or relationship with the adult world. In some aspects of childhood, such as dolls, this is very fully developed and has a special section devoted to ethnographical specimens, such as fertility and magic dolls, votive figures, costume and boudoir dolls and similar pieces.

Normally the Museum is concerned solely with the British child, but toys are international, so there is hardly a country which is not represented. Special attention has always been paid to acquiring Asiatic toys made during the Empire period, and to all forms of true folk or home-made toys.

All items on public exhibition are well documented, notably the Scottish "Mansion in Miniature", the famous Doll's House known as Stanbrig Eorls, created by the late Miss Graham Montgomery, last of the Montcrieffes of Montcrieff, in 1885. Begun in 1885, the House was developed over seventy years and the furnishings are well-nigh perfect in all thirteen rooms, attics, staircases and landings.

On sale is a well-produced descriptive Handbook, breakdowns of the exhibits into sections and with a continuity that links them to the basic thematic concept of childhood.

There are also picture postcards and colour slides available.

DUMFRIES BURGH MUSEUM
THE OBSERVATORY, CORBERRY HILL, DUMFRIES.

Open:

April to September: *Weekdays (except Tuesday)*, 10—1;

Sunday, 2—6.   2—7.

October to March: *Weekdays only*, 10—1; 2—5.

The Museum devotes one room to the subject of Victorian childhood in the area.

This section has been growing for seven or eight years. The room is in the basement of a 1798 stone windmill, which contains a variety of toys—doll's cheesepress, doll's savings bank, doll's parasol, teasets and similar items, plus many games and a wide and growing range of children's books—in addition to dress, educational and social material and a large selection of photographs of local children, going back to the 1850s.

The largest items are two rocking horses, one of them over a century old. The room is semi-circular, roughly twelve feet along its straight wall and ten feet across to the curved wall; as much of the material as possible is displayed open, but there are a hundred or so items in desk-cases, and the collection of 11 dolls and two Arks dating from the 1850s, a "walking" horse and cart, and a dwarf-and-goat savings bank are in an alcove in the wall behind polythene.

Other Scottish Collections may be seen at the following places: —

The "Old Glasgow" Museum and Art Gallery, People's Palace, Glasgow, S.E.

1. Children's toys.
2. Games.
3. Clothes.
4. Books.
5. Costume dolls from various parts of the world. (Eunice Murray collection.)
6. Case illustrating the story of Cock Robin.

Dick Institute, Kilmarnock.

1. Hinching: nine hinching (stone) balls of varying size used in game where the ball is "thrown athwart the hip over a chosen course". Game popular last century in Ayrshire and North-East Scotland.
2. Indian figures: Set of 13 Indian mythological figures for use in miniature theatre. Figures in wood, coloured.
3. Musical glasses: Set of 25 glasses with manual.
4. Handbells: Two silver handbells.
5. Gaming boards: One oriental and one African board. Semi-circular grooves made into the board to hold stakes. Coloured dice use dfor numbers.
6. Assorted figures: Twelve Egyptian painted figures, two Chinese, to represent workers. Wooden and coloured.

Glenesk Trust Folk Museum, Retreat Lodge, Glenesk, Brechin, Angus.

1. Clothes (19th century).
2. Chair, cradles, stools.
3. Books.
4. Schools Section, including Text-books.
5. Dolls.
6. Doll's House, with Edwardian furniture.

7. Doll's China, Cradle, etc.
8. Other toys.
9. Musical Boxes.
10. Scrap-work Draught Screens.
11. Samplers.
12. Photographs.

HIGHLAND FOLK MUSEUM, ANN FASGADH, KINGUSSIE, INVERNESSSHIRE.
1. Toys and possessions.
2. Documents concerning old schools of the north and west, and on the rearing of children in the past.
3. Pieces of children's furniture.
4. Christening clothes.
5. Pottery ornaments of child subjects.

THE MUSEUM, 1 HIGH STREET, ELGIN, MORAYSHIRE.
Miniature Carpenter's Shop in a glass case. (Puppets: working model.)

THE FACTOR, ATHOLL ESTATES OFFICE, BLAIR ATHOLL PERTHSHIRE.
1. Victorian and Georgian toys: Jig-saw puzzles (geographical).
2. Playing cards.
3. Magic lanterns and slides.
4. Playing card games (musical).

ART GALLERY & INDUSTRIAL MUSEUM, ABERDEEN.
1. Victorian bricks.
2. Built-up pictures of the "jig-saw" type.
3. Miniature utensils.

HOPETOUN ESTATES OFFICE, SOUTH QUEENSFERRY, WEST LOTHIAN.
1. A beautifully-painted small donkey-cart.
2. Various models.
3. A Wendy house in the policies, etc.
4. Quite a number of things to do with children.

WALES

AMGUEDDFA GENEDLAETHOL CYMRU
(NATIONAL MUSEUM OF WALES)
CATHAYS PARK, CARDIFF, GLAMORGAN.

Open: *Weekdays,* 10—5.
      Sunday, 2.30—5.
      Thursdays, April to September; Bank Holidays and
      Tuesdays following, 10—8.
Admission: *Weekdays, Free; Sundays,* 6d.

The famous Lovett Collection of Dolls, formerly housed in this Museum, has been transferred to the Museum of Childhood, Edinburgh (*q.v., page* 62).

The principal remaining specimens from this Collection are : —

    A small fragmentary pottery doll, said to be from a child's grave at Sandy (Beds.).
    Copy of a jointed Greek doll of terracotta.
    Two large 18th century costume dolls.
    A very fine large costume doll of C1860.
    An early 19th century "pedlar-woman" doll.
    A Congo fetish doll.
    Punch and Judy puppets.
    Foreign folk costume dolls, of recent date.

AMGUEDDFA WERIN CYMRU
(WELSH FOLK MUSEUM)
ST. FAGAN'S CASTLE, CARDIFF.

Admission Free.

This famous Welsh collection, which owes much to the work of its Curator, Dr. Iorwerth C. Peate, possesses many items of juvenile interest which are exhibited in appropriate context. A recent listing by the Assistant Keeper is as follows: —

Fifty dolls and accessories, some in Welsh costume, mostly from 19th century.

Dancing doll on spring board.

Doll's clothing.

Dolls' houses (two) with contents, 19th century.

Dolls' tea sets.

Model farmyard (stable, horses, cowhouse, cows, pig, wagon and driver, sacks, hay-rack, harrow).

Rush toys.

Toy soldiers, wooden and tin, and fortress.

Sword toy.

Spinning top.

Whirligigs (two).

Hopscotch stone.

Wooden top.

Whistle.

Mechanical toy, C1870.

"Victoria Cross Gallery" (cut-out toy).

Toy donkey.

Kaleidoscope.

Collection of puppets and props relating to Matio Puppet Players (1928-1945).

Musical jug, plays Llwyn Onn (1936).

Musical boxes (four), second half, 19th century.

Seraphone, automatic.

Other Toys in Welsh Museums

There are several token collections hitherto not classified, among them some noteworthy specimens in the Museums at Brecon and Carmarthen.

*   *   *

PART II

DOLLS, DOLL'S HOUSES, DOLL CLUBS, SPECIAL EXHIBITIONS

(A) SPECIAL DOLL COLLECTIONS AT: —
Victoria & Albert Museum, London, S.W.7.
Barry Elder Doll Museum, London, W.8.
Queen's Park Gallery, Harpurhey, Manchester.
Oken's House, Warwick.

(B) DOLLS' HOUSES IN: —
Public Collections.
Private Collections.
Brighton (The Batty Doll's House).
Gorey (Eire) ("Titania's Palace").
Oxford (The Rotunda, Iffley Turn).
Windsor (The Queen's Dolls' House).

(C) DOLL CLUBS
Doll Club of Great Britain.
Dollmakers' Circle.

(D) SPECIAL EXHIBITIONS MOUNTED IN RECENT YEARS

THE COSTUME COURT,
THE VICTORIA AND ALBERT MUSEUM
CROMWELL ROAD, LONDON, S.W.7.
Open: Weekdays, 10—6; Sundays, 2.30—6.
Admission Free.

The Victoria and Albert Museum contains one of the world's outstanding collections of costume, both actual dresses and accessories, as well as costume illustration.

The Court shows only fashionable costume (men's and women's) from about 1580 to 1947, and includes both English and Continental clothes.

On display are some 120 full costumes with their accessories, as well as about 600 separately displayed accessories from all periods. There is also a small but important collection of costume dolls.

The dolls are exhibited in a large case, accessible from all four sides, situated opposite Cases 25 and 26—only a few from a large representative collection.

Each doll has been chosen because it is wearing—unaltered —the clothes of its period. Some dolls were simply prestige playthings, like the rare wooden doll of 1690-1700, and the finely modelled wax doll dressed in the fashions of 1787; but others seem less ingenuous about their role of miniature mannequin. None, so far as we know, is an actual *poupée modèle,* sent by a milliner to acquaint her customers with the latest fashions; but the bride doll is marked "Mrs. Powell's wedding suit 1761", aid comes from a series of dolls which succeeding generations of the Powell family from 1756 to 1912 dressed to show the fashions of their times, other examples from this collection being also shown here. There is a wooden doll provided with formal and informal clothes, which is marked on the body "dressed in the fashion 1763". All these dolls are as fully clothed as their human counterparts, but fortunately they cannot be as discreet about the secrets of their wardrobes, so that they provide a unique series of accessories and underwear for us to study. The shifts, bodices, petticoats and hats from the chest-of-drawers of the 1747 dolls' house—in their miniature perfection—can only be compared with the contents of the best 17th century Dutch *puppenhuizen,* or the famous German dolls' house of the Princess Augusta Dorothea von Schwartzburg-Arnstadt (C1745).

Also, to judge by the wardrobes of early 19th century dolls, it would seem that they were wearing drawers some 55 years before ladies are recorded as doing so.

THE BARRY ELDER DOLL MUSEUM
114 GLENTHORNE ROAD, HAMMERSMITH, LONDON, W.8.

Open: Daily, 10—6.

Admission 2/6.

THE QUEEN'S PARK ART GALLERY
HARPURHEY, MANCHESTER.

Open: Weekdays, 10—8 (10—6, *or dusk, in Winter*).

Sundays, 2.30—8 (2.30—5, *or dusk, in Winter*).

Admission Free.

This Gallery and Museum, administered by the Corporation of Manchester normally exhibits paintings, sculpture and the drawings of the last hundred years. It is also the home of the famous Greg Collection of playthings of the past. This includes some antique toys like cup-and-ball, etc., but it comprises mainly period dolls, dolls' houses and accessories of all kinds.

On the left of the door as we come in are many small objects, such as miniature books, watering cans and models of furniture with fruit, cutlery and crockery on the tables. Not all the furniture was made for dolls' houses—some was made as proof that an apprentice had learnt his trade as a cabinet maker. In the window are three girls sitting in small rooms of their own—the last one is supposed to be Queen

Adelaide, by the way, and although her silk dress is tattered, the dressing table at which she sits is a splended one. Coming down the room you see the furnished houses; one has a curved staircase, another one has an old front that might have been designed by Robert Adam. They are all furnished in the style of particular periods with dolls dressed to match. The Victorian house has a basement with plain wooden chairs and a dining room above with elegant polished ones. The 18th century house has less furniture, as was usual at the time. In all the houses there are many amusing and interesting details of furniture, figures and decorations. In the same row as the houses, stands a greengrocer's shop with all sorts of modelled fruit and vegetables.

At the end wall is an empty house, unrestored, which is so carefully made that it must have been an architect's model. Next to it are items are dolls' clothing, and next to them, facing the window some of the dolls, mostly dressed in the elaborate fashions of the 19th century. There are evening dresses and day dresses; there is a bride in white, a country girl, a poor girl with boots on, and one beautiful doll in a golden dress who may be French and as old as the 17th century.

In the centre of the room are some more dolls' houses and furnished rooms. There is a large fine bedroom and smaller houses with furniture of different periods. Almost everything on display was given by Mrs. T. T. Greg, a great collector and lover of old things, for whose generosity children in Manchester and elsewhere have been grateful.

DOLLS' MUSEUM
OKEN'S HOUSE, CASTLE STREET, WARWICK.

Open: Weekdays, 10—6.

Sunday, 2.30—5.

Admission, 1/-; Children, 6d.

Mrs. Joy Robinson, owner of this remarkable Collection of period dolls, founder of the Museum, and resident Curator, tells how it all started—just out of her childhood love of dolls.

" As a child of course, like all little girls, I had my dolls, and to me they were my children whom I dressed and undressed and put to bed. I talked to them and when I was in disgrace, cried to them, just as so many children have done through the ages, and as I suppose they still do. At that time, these were just my playthings and that was all, until one day (a wet day as I remember) I was playing in the attic at my mother's house.

" In the attic was an old chest, and pulling out the bottom drawer, I saw a lovely old doll—quite different from the ones I daily played with. She lay there amongst moth balls, with an old faded brown parasol as her only companion. This doll—Emily by name—was the very one my great grandmother played with in those spacious days of the mid-nineteenth century, when the Great Exhibition of 1851 was the talk of London and the wonder of the world. Mother said that I could have 'Emily', and it was having her that really made me want to start to collect, and as I collected, to study these old dolls of an age gone by. Since then I have lost no opportunity to add to my collection, and during the passing years I have cherished an ambition to share my dolls and my knowledge of them, by putting them on permanent exhibition in a museum devoted exclusively to old dolls and their history.

"In this museum is my ambition realized, and here I hope you will find not only dolls, but a link with the children of the past".

The Joy Robinson Collection is displayed according to the following groupings: —

(a) Wooden Dolls of varied range.

(b) Wax Playdolls, mainly English and French.

(c) Porcelain, or "china" Dolls, including specimens with parian or bisque heads.

(d) "Automatic" Dolls.

The latter, known popularly as "moving dolls", date from the late 18th and early 19th centuries. These were actuated either by turning a crank, or later by clockwork. Music boxes, and even barrel-organs or hurdy-gurdies were sometimes incorporated in the mechanisms, to give joy to all who heard and saw them. The Warwick Doll Museum collection contains specimens of clockwork walking dolls of the year 1862— a doll with a monkey's face which plays a fiddle, taps his foot, turns his head and opens his mouth while a hurdy-gurdy plays a series of tunes. This is of French origin, and is very early 19th century. There are several musical dancing dolls, and many other interesting automata in the Museum.

The collection is added to each year.

An illustrated booklet giving the story of the collection and historical synopses on all the groups above-mentioned is on sale.

"*There were houses in it, finished and unfinished, for dolls of all stations in life. Suburban tenements for dolls of moderate means; kitchens and single apartments for dolls of the lower classes; capital town residences for dolls of high estate. Some of these establishments were already furnished according to estimate, with a view to the convenience of the dolls of limited income; others could be fitted in the most expensive scale, at a moment's notice, from whole shelves of chairs and tables, sofas, bedsteads, and upholstery.*

"*In the midst of all these objects Caleb and his daughter sat at work. The blind girl busy as a doll's dressmaker; Caleb painting and glazing the four-pair front of a desirable family mansion.*

"'*There we are,' said Caleb, falling back a pace or two to form the better judgment of his work; ' as near the real thing as six penn'orth of halfpence is to sixpence.'*"

CHARLES DICKENS: " The Cricket on the Hearth."

ABOUT DOLLS' HOUSES

Among the more beautiful playthings which have found their way into our national collections are dolls' houses.

Passed on from one generation to another with loving care, many fine examples of period houses and their miniature accessories have now become showpieces enjoyed by an ever-growing public. In fact, our visitors (particularly from the United States and Canada, where there exists a widespread interest in this topic) make a special point of seeing some of our dolls' houses while touring the country.

We are fortunate in having what is probably the most famous example of the craftsman's miniature art, Queen Mary's Dolls' House. This may be seen at Windsor Castle, Berkshire, throughout the year, except when the Court is in residence. It is reached by the same entrance as that leading to the State Apartments, and the additional fee of sixpence goes to a charity. It is estimated from from eighty to a hundred thousand people every year go to look at this tiny three-dimensional record of our century. It is perfect down to the last detail and was designed by Sir Edwin Lutyens.

It was "made with devotion and the utmost skill as a loyal gift" to Her Majesty the late Queen Mary, and was exhibited at the British Empire Exhibition of 1924. Among its many marvellous details it boasts a garage housing a fleet of model cars, including a Rolls-Royce. The books in its library, although not larger than a postage stamp, were written specially by eminent men of letters and reduced to microscopic dimensions. All the pictures and portraits on the walls were painted by leading artists, and the most famous designers of the day planned the furniture, decorations, kitchenware and each small detail in the fittings.

Queen Mary was a great collector of miniature objects and presented many gifts to our national museums. Today we may admire one of these, a doll's house fully furnished in the mid-Victorian manner, in the Children's Room of the London Museum at Kensington Palace. This is a most appropriate place, because it was here that the youthful Queen Victoria played with her toys before her accession, and in a neighbouring showcase are displayed the wooden dolls as dressed by the young princess.

Another institution which has benefited from Queen Mary's generosity is the Victoria and Albert Museum. Part of its collection, which may be seen at its branch in Bethnal Green, East London, is graced by another royal gift. The dolls' house at the Bethnal Green Museum which they regard as most rare, however, is an English model dating from about 1760. It measures 5′ 1″ on its stand of 2′. It is 4′ 10″ wide and 3′ 6″ in depth. The façade, a perfect replica of the English Georgian style of architecture, swings open to reveal rooms and furniture to scale.

A fully equipped period dolls' house, when it is made by a skilled master craftsman, holds more than antiquarian interest for us. It teaches us something of the domestic customs and patterns of family life; the social graces, arts and entertainments. Because the child invests her world with replicas of full-scale objects, many are charming architectural records of the styles through which our stately mansions and elegant middle-class homes have passed during the reigns of no less than ten British monarchs.

Dolls' houses, surprisingly, have been in existence for no longer than three centuries. In the seventeenth century they were called "baby houses", massive affairs set on legs liks china cabinets. About 5′ long, including their frames, they were divided symmetrically into four rooms. A very famous one is the Westbrook Baby House. It was made in 1705 by a group of local tradesmen, who presented it to little Miss E. Westbrook, the child of a property owner who was then leaving their district, the Isle of Dogs. It has passed down through the female line to its present owner, Mrs. Cyril Holland-Martin. Private owners frequently present, or bequeath, such treasures to local museums.

Playing with dolls' houses was every small girl's delight during Queen Victoria's reign. Therefore, the largest number of survivors date from this, and the Edwardian, periods. Models in the early, middle and late Victorian styles may be seen at Gunnersbury Park Museum, West London; Maidstone Museum, Kent; Blaise Castle, Bristol; and other regional centres. At the Castle Museum in York, which boats a celebrated collection of playthings of the past, at Kirkstall Museum, Leeds, and at the Bowes Museum at Barnard Castle, County Durham, they have some fine examples. I recently spotted a mid-Victorian house at Salford Art Gallery, Lancashire, which is taller than an average eight-year-old child. But the most enchanting hours I have spent looking at these curiosities were passed at Queen's Park, Manchester. There they have set out the accessories and furniture as early as Queen Anne in single showcases, representing rooms exquisitely in period. These treasures include many dolls' houses and a splendid Nuremberg kitchen, which was made in 1870 for the Mrs. Gregg who bestowed them. Another keen collector, Major Rowland Winn, is the donor of a very special dolls' house, which fills visitors to Nostell Priory, Wakefield, Yorkshire, with admiration. Its miniature chairs and tables are all of Chippendale design, an unusual feature.

Perhaps the most wonderfully elegant building of this kind which the visitor to Britain may see is the Georgian doll's house at Uppark, Sussex, owned by the National Trust. Mr. Christopher Hussey tells how this was made about 1730 for Sarah, only daughter of Christopher Lethieullier, of Belmont, Middlesex. It has a long and romantic history, and must have made a lasting impression on H. G. Wells when he was a boy, because he later described it at great length in his novel *Tono Bungay*. It was at Uppark that his mother had been housekeeper when he was a small child.

FAMOUS DOLLS' HOUSES AND BABY HOUSES
IN PUBLIC COLLECTIONS

In addition to Dolls' Houses listed under the Museum Collections (to which occasional acquistions, by gift, purchase and bequest make the keeping of an entirely up-to-date index impracticable), the following have a special interest for those who admire this legacy from our architectural past: —

The Blackett Baby House (1740); The Lansdowne Dolls' House (1860) and The "Princess May of Teck" Dolls' House (1880), are all in the custody of The London Museum, Kensington Palace. In the State Apartments of the same building one may view Queen Victoria's Baby House (1825).

The Victoria and Albert Museum now has on loan The Drew Dolls' House (1860-65), while Bethnal Green Museum has in safe keeping at least six important examples, i.e.: —

The Tate Baby House (1760); The Denton Welch Baby House (1783); The Thornton Smith House (1800); Caroline Cottage—Abergeldie (1831); Mrs. Greg's Own House (1840); and Miss Miles' House (1890).

In the North of England spectacular examples have been added to the Museums at York (*page* 59), Leeds (*page* 44) and to the Museum of Childhood, Edinburgh (*page* 63).

At the Bowes Museum, Barnard Castle, there is a fine example of a Yorkshire Set of Rooms (1820).

BABY HOUSES AND DOLLS' HOUSES—PRIVATELY OWNED

Anne Sharp's Baby House, 1690-1700, owned by Mrs. E. A. Bulwer.

The Westlake Baby House, 1705, owned by Mrs. Cyril Holland Martin.

A Travelling Baby House; a mid-Georgian House and Garden; and a late Georgian Baby House; owned by Wythenshawe Hall.

The Ditchley House, 1734, owned by Trustees of the Bodleian Library, Oxford.

Scadbury Manor Baby House, 1730, owned by Mrs. Andrews.

Nostell Priory, 1740, owned by Major Rowland Winn.

The Manwaring House, 1788, owned by J. Manwaring Baines, Esq.

The Pearwood Pavilion, 1780, owned by Mr. and Mrs. Lesley Gooden.

Amelia's House, C1790, owned by Lady Maxwell.

The Evans Baby House, C1750, owned by Rev. and Mrs. W. J. S. Weir.

Clifton Castle, 1810, owned by Col. Curzon-Howe-Herrick.

Stack House, 1820, owned by Mrs. Mary Titcombe.

The Fry Dolls' House, 1836, owned by Mrs. Bates-Harbin.

Clare Wing's Dolls' House, 1830-40, owned by Mrs. C. A. Greene.

Weston Hall, 1835, owned by Sacheverell Sitwell, Esq.

Knayton Lodge, Thirsk, owned by Mrs. Haggie.

Tickenhill (I), 1852, owned by J. F. Parker, Esq.

The Sherborne Dolls' House, 1870, owned by Mrs. O. A. Clarke.

The Longleat Dolls' House, 1870, owned by The Marquess of Bath.

The Henderson Dolls' House, 1890+, owned by Mrs. Alan Henderson.

Dingley Hall, 1874, owned by Mrs. Alexandra Currie.

The above-listed historical specimens, being privately-owned, are not on view to members of the public. These, and others not listed, are fully described and when possible illustrated, in Vivien Greene's standard reference book on the subject, *English Dolls' Houses*, published, B. T. Batsford. The author is in touch with private owners and is willing to advise specialists and students who write to her at The Rotunda (*see page* 88).

Miniature Sets of Rooms, Privately Owned

18th Century Salon (French). From the Helena Rubinstein Collection, New York, on view at the Rubinstein Beauty Salon, 3 Grafton Street, Mayfair, London, W.1.

Mrs. Carlisle, The Pitt House, Ashampstead, Berkshire.

Mrs. Warne, Flat 10, 38 Granville Road, Bath Road, Reading, Berkshire.

THE BATTY DOLLS' HOUSE
West Pier, Brighton, Sussex.

Opening Hours: June (Whitsuntide) to September, 8—10, and on specially fine days, out of season.
Admission to the Pier, 6d. Admission to the Batty and Richold Collections, 6d.
Descriptive Booklets and souvenir colour postcards on sale.

Not many Exhibition sites are as salubrious as a holiday pier, with the salt waters gently swirling under one's feet. Such is the location where an Exhibition of famous show-pieces has come to rest for the past sixteen years, having toured almost every part of the country and given untold pleasure to thousands.

A step from the promenade at Brighton takes one on to the West Pier, and at the furthermost end, just before one reaches the sea-fishing "pitches", and well-sheltered, are the Exhibition Rooms.

The first of these (admission free) houses the famous Richold Collection of models. They are mainly of architectural interest and were made by Richard Old, a Yorkshire cabinet-maker and organ-builder who worked in Middlesbrough (1856-1932), devoting every hour of his leisure to his hobby. Every one of the 767 models shown, is a labour of love, executed from fine woods with a fret-saw by one of the world's superb craftsmen. His Milan Cathedral (scale 1 in 100), is a currently valued at £20,000 and is constructed from 8,000 separate pieces. Other replicas of famous buildings ("Toys for architects?") include Ulm Cathedral; The Giotto Campanile, Florence; and our own St. Paul's, London.

Toy-lovers who have also a fondness for model-making cannot fail to delight in several items such as the following exquisitely-fashioned pieces as numbered in the Catalogue: —

No. 6.   Old State Carriage of France, carved in satin walnut.
No. 21.   Engine and Tender.
No. 58.   A scale model Dolls' House, in English white chestnut and satin walnut.
No. 67.   A double-deck tramcar.
No. 83.   Another Dolls' House.
and
No. 162.   A Vintage Motor car.

On Wednesdays and Saturdays on duty with the Collection is Mrs. H. Todd, who knew the late craftsman and who is familiar with every iota of his workmanship. She is always pleased to chat to serious visitors about individual pieces, and she has virtually "lived with" these treasures on Brighton Pier since 1950.

During the years when they were on tour she acquired another unique item, a little masterpiece in its way, made by a Mr. Pridmore, a working jeweller, with a reputation in his native Winchester, Hampshire. This is a Miniature House of four rooms (panelled), approximately 12″ x 8″, two landings and a kitchen, containing in all 220 silver toys or, in collectors' parlance, "silver miniatures".

Every object is of hand-wrought silver, magnificently executed. Mr. Pridmore's skill was not confined to reproducing period furniture of a wide range (note, the wheelback chairs and four-poster bed), but he has contrived to create the illusion of cloth and fabric out of delicate silverwork in such things as the towel on its rail, the curtains hanging on the windows, and the staircase carpets.

THE BATTY DOLLS' HOUSE

All of these whet one's appetite for the *piece-de-resistance*, curtained off in a room to itself within the Model Pavilion— the Batty Dolls' House. This is the creation of another remarkable and modest Yorkshireman, the late Mr. T. Batty of Drighlington, near Bradford. He began work on it in 1908 and, before he died in 1933, had the satisfaction of experiencing widespread acclaim when the House went on tour all over the country. Already acquiring the *ambience* of a period piece, although it is strictly a twentieth-century masterpiece, it is described as being the only serious rival in craftsmanship to the Queen's Dolls' House at Windsor (*page* 90). To plan, construct and finish the house took Mr. Batty over twenty-two years, half a lifetime's tireless work of unrelaxing patience and infinite skill.

The four carpets in the house, for example, took Mr. Batty two years to make, working on an average of eight hours a day. *It is estimated that in each there are 2,400,000 threads.* In one cross stitch carpet alone the needle must have passed through the canvas 200,000 times. The finished effects, though, are stunning in the clearness of the pattern and the excellence of their colouring and design. They have wrung superlative praise from one of the leading carpet manufacturers of this country.

It is really impossible to describe in detail everything which can be seen in the four rooms and magnificent hall and landing of the house.

After seeing all the rooms finished with miniature but strong model furniture, all accurate in scale and detail of workmanship, one frequently has difficulty in deciding which room appeals most, for each has a different kind of beauty.

The exterior of the house, too, has a number of interesting features. Special among these is a device of Mr. Batty's own invention whereby the chimneys can be swept without entering the respective rooms. A portion of the exterior wall is constructed separately, and may be removed as a unit to enable the chimney-sweep to tackle his job from the outside.

Taking a final look around this miniature house, which took almost half a lifetime to build and equip, one cannot but feel that it is a little monument to a master craftsman to whom time and trouble meant nothing if there were beauty and permanency to show at the finish. It tells a little epic of a man who loved his work.

"TITANIA'S PALACE"
BALLYNASTRAGH, GOREY, COUNTY WEXFORD,
(The home of the Countess of Wicklow).
THE REPUBLIC OF IRELAND.

Admission: *Daily*.

Travel: By road from Dublin and Arklow (County Wicklow), turn right at Tinnock Railway Bridge, then second left turn.

Token Donations go to children's charities and have already totalled well over £80,000.

Literature: A fully descriptive, room-by-room, Illustrated Handbook, price 1/- (40 pp.), is on sale at Ballynastragh House, written by Major Sir Nevile Wilkinson who invented, designed and decorated the Palace.

Yvette In Italy and Titania's Palace (Wilkinson) with twenty-four illustrations, was first published by Hodder & Stoughton in 1922, but now out of print.

Titania's Palace, said to be the most beautiful and richly-furnished Dolls' House in the world, is now accommodated in the home of Lady Wicklow, in County Wexford. It was first placed on view in London on July 6th, 1922, opened by the late Queen Mary at the Women's Exhibition at Olympia.

Since then it has visited 160 cities in the United Kingdom, Ireland, the United States, South America, Australia, New Zealand and Canada. More than 1,800,000 people have admired this masterpiece of miniature perfection and which now draws numbers of visitors every week.

They are shown its wealth of miniature works of art and craftsmanship by the Dowager Countess of Wicklow, or when she is away, by her younger daughter. Sir Nevile Wilkinson, Architect-in-Chief of Titania's Palace, was Lady Wicklow's first husband. Their elder daughter, who saw the fairy, is now a Sister devoting her life to the welfare of children in England.

It is to children that the palace is dedicated, for though no charge is made for admission, most callers leave something in the collecting box for "sick, crippled and unhappy children of the world, irrespective of creed and colour".

Built in Hicks' workshop in Dublin, the Palace itself takes up most of a large room of Ballynastragh House, and its eight sections completely fill a four-ton steel lift van. Its ground plan covers sixty-three square feet and its height, above the raised platform that makes inspection easy, is twenty-seven inches. The belfry, with its peal of sweet-chiming bells, is by Lutyens.

But it is the contents of the sixteen rooms (containing well over 10,000 individual pieces of tiny-craft ancient and modern), that most delight both children and adults. Many were specially made, others collected by Sir Nevile, and others acquired on the travels of the Palace.

A gold nugget is a gift made in Ballarat. The green malachite kiwi comes from New Zealand; the gold beaver, a present from Canada. Children are thrilled by the tiny bicycle in the Entrance Hall; the pram that Shirley Temple —then an eight-year-old filmstar—insisted on wheeling; the miniscule unscrewable electric bulbs (as used in doctors' pencil torches) that light up the rooms, the fairy doll's-house within a doll's-house, the clock down which the mouse ran, and the wee (it's the only word!) toothbrushes of the Princesses Iris and Ruby.

Adults come away with a confused feeling of *embarras de richesse,* remembering mainly articles like the tiny gold figures by Benvenuto Cellini on the arms of the throne, into the back of which is set a diamond brooch that belonged to the Empress Eugenie; the sixteenth-century boxwood Holy Family from South Germany and the exquisite little illuminated Book of Hours (C1450) in the Chapel; fine ivory carvings in the Royal bedchamber, once handled by pretty, witty Nell Gwynn; a tiny enamel horse found in an Egyptian mummy case 3,000 years old; and—American visitors exult to hear this —a slip of vitrified mastodon bone splinter from Denver, Colorado, beneath the throne which is certainly the oldest object in the treasure house.

There is an organ that can be played with matchsticks; the world's smallest rosary; the world's smallest collar-stud (perfectly turned in ivory and almost as invisible as its owner, King Oberon); a library of miniature books and newspapers; General Tom Thumb's visiting card; famous signatures in the visitors' book including those of Royalty and Charlie Chaplin.

Many miniature paintings and all the mosaic painting on the ceilings (there are 250,000 dots in the bathroom alone) are the work of Sir Nevile, who continued adding to the decorations until his death. Irish and foreign craftsmen contributed such pieces as reproductions of the Ardagh Chalice, the Cross of Cong, bronze doorways, stained glass windows, furniture delicately wrought in many styles. And Lady Wicklow herself planted the flowers—made from Woolworth's hat-trimmings in the days of "nothing over sixpence"—in the central courtyard.

What is it all worth in hard cash? Lady Wicklow has no idea. She has come to the conclusion that, being irreplaceable, it is beyond price—like the pleased excitement and delight of the children to whom she loves to explain the absence of chimneys; "Fairy fires are made by glow-worms". Being practical as well as romantic, she has turned the palace and its contents into a limited company, Tinycraft, Ltd., so that it may still be giving pleasure to boys and girls and their elders and collecting money for less fortunate children when she is gone.

THE ROTUNDA
A MUSEUM OF PERIOD DOLLS' HOUSES
GROVE HOUSE, IFFLEY TURN, OXFORD.

Opening Times: *Two Sunday afternoons in each summer month, or at other times for parties of 10 or more, if sufficient written notice be given. Visitors under 16 NOT admitted, whether accompanied by an adult or not.*

This collections of Dolls' Houses, privately owned by Mrs. Graham Greene, is concerned with the architecture and furnishings of the past. It consists of 26 examples dating from C1700 to 1886, is necessarily incomplete, and any offers to lend (or sell) baby houses or dolls' houses of a kind not yet represented would be warmly welcomed. All expenses and insurance would be undertaken, and careful maintenance in a new, well-warmed building is assured. Such houses should be free of woodworm, but need not necessarily be furnished. All houses are regularly examined and treated.

It will be noticed that the Museum is not expected to interest children. Its appeal will be to collectors and to those who like to observe how the fashion in furniture and fabric, which of course closely reflects social life and attitudes, is copied (allowing for the inevitable time-lag) in that small counterpart of the English home, the English doll's house.

So many people came to see the eighteenth century Baby Houses and the nineteenth century dolls' houses at Grove House that a Rotunda, the first in Oxford since 1749, has been built to contain the collection; it can now be shown more easily and with better lighting than was possible before. A spiral iron staircase, once part of the old St. James's Theatre demolished in 1960, leads to a circular gallery where the smaller dolls' houses stand and where a replica of an eighteenth century shop window contains changing displays.

Here are shown different kinds of toy kitchen implements, including those now out of use, such as cheese-toasters, "hasteners", bottle-jacks, dripping pans, Etnas for boiling water, copper moulds and fish-kettles. Besides these there are numbers of forgotten domestic objects such as foot-warmers heated by charcoal, tinder-boxes, taper-stands, sad-irons and the varieties of portable bath, all from dolls' houses.

With the dinner services are shown the glass and metal epergnes that, piled with fruit and fern, crowned the table, and the bewitching dishes of food; bewitching, that is, to see in miniature but unappetising, we should now think, in reality; one especially remembers the whole boiled rabbit with its ears and teeth and the complete calf's head with its eyes "cooked in the German manner".

The evolving taste in furnishings can of course be seen in the dolls' houses themselves, particularly the important social change that occurred when the flat woodburning hearth gave place to the high narrow grate and the poker came into the house with sea-coal. Or we can see the difference between the early square fortepiano with its reversal of the modern black and white keys and the upright piano of 1880 with a painted silk front embellished with flying cranes in the "japonais" style then admired.

Reference should be made however briefly to the pieces of eighteenth and nineteenth century wallpapers so often found in dolls' houses; some are shown revealed, with later papers removed: others too fragmentary to keep are displayed separately.

QUEEN MARY'S DOLLS' HOUSE
WINDSOR CASTLE, WINDSOR, BERKSHIRE.

The Castle Precincts are open daily throughout the year from 10 a.m. to sunset.

Admission Free.
The State Apartments

The State Apartments are shown to the public, the nett proceeds of the admission fees being devoted to charity. They are open daily on weekdays (Monday to Saturday inclusive), and, during the Summer months only, on Sunday afternoons. The State Apartments are closed when Her Majesty is in residence; which usually, but not always, entails their closure during the month of April, and for periods during the months of March, May and June.

Times of Opening are: —

Weekdays:

1st November to 31st March	...	...	11—3
1st April to 31st May	...	...	11—4
1st June to 30th September	...	...	11—5
1st October to 31st October	...	...	11—4

Sundays:

May to September	...	...	...	1.30—5
October	...	...	...	1—4

Queen Mary's Dolls' House can be seen on the same conditions as the State Apartments.

The Queen's Dolls' House at Windsor Castle (when shown during the absence of the Court) is open to the public on Monday to Saturday inclusive, and during the summer months on Sunday afternoons. A charge of sixpence each person is made for admission. Tickets are never issued in advance.

The Souvenir Book and Postcards of the Dolls' House are on sale at the bookstalls within the precincts, at 2/-.

The public who wish to view the Queen's Dolls' House will approach through the entrance on the North Terrace and, on the way to the Dolls' House, pass two cases filled with interesting miniature objects which have been given to her Majesty, but for which there is no room in the Dolls' House itself.

The Queen's Dolls' House is now permanently housed at Windsor Castle. It occupies the room which was once a China Room beneath the Throne Room, and has been adapted by Sir Edwin Lutyens, R.A.

The Dolls' House is arranged so that the public may walk with ease right round it, and is preserved by a glass case covering the whole.

Around the walls is a shelf upon which stand miniature houses in the same style and to the same scale as the Dolls' House proper. These houses contain interesting little oddments, supplementing those in the Dolls' House.

The walls have been prepared with great care and concern for permanence, for the beautiful landscape mural paintings by Philip Connard, R.A. These consist of pictorial views of the Royal Palaces of Windsor, St. James's, Hampton Court, and Buckingham Palace.

To give Her Majesty a Doll's House more perfect than any Dolls' House had ever been before— in whose ingenious brain this inspiration first had birth is mystery rather than history. But this we know as fact, that had that idea not enkindled a flame in the creative mind of Sir Edwin Lutyens, the House most probably would never have been built at all, and certainly would not be the miracle of fine workmanship that it is.

When Sir Edwin Landseer Lutyens was born, the world was enriched by a new wonder: an eternal child, an apostle of beauty, an apostle of thoroughness, a minister of elvish nonsense, all in one. He built the new Delhi, eighty square miles of palace and avenue; he built the Cenotaph; that sublime memorial of British courage, British devotion, and British sacrifice; he built the Queen's Dolls' House, an affair of inches, but such an affair as not even the Japanese cherrystone carvers could excel.

This composite creation by a team of brilliant artists and craftsmen is fully described in two large volumes. Written by experts and connoisseurs they are entitled respectively *The Book of The Queen's Dolls' House* and *The Library of The Queen's Dolls' House* and are themselves part of the national gift. *The Souvenir Book,* which is on sale to visitors, published by gracious permission of Her Majesty The Queen, is composed of significant excerpts from the larger volumes. Chapter headings include the following themes: The Story of the Gift; Its Historical Value; Its Playful Aspect; The Beauty and Difficulty of Smallness; The Architecture, described Room by Room; The Garden; Games; and The Garage. *The Souvenir Book* contains some seventy pages and has several halftone photographs of such aspects as The King's Bedroom; The Queen's Bedroom; The Library; The Linen Room; The Wine Cellar and The Butler's Pantry.

In addition to this publication, postcard reproductions in colour are available at 3/- per packet.

THE DOLL CLUB OF GREAT BRITAIN
12 THE CLOSE, NEW MALDEN, SURREY, ENGLAND.

In July, 1953, a group of plangonologists gathered together and formed the Doll Club of Great Britain, the first British Doll Club.

Club Committee:
  President:
    Mrs. Graham Greene.
  Vice-Chairmen:
    Miss R. Ferguson.
    Miss F. Eaton.
  Hon. Secretary:
    Mrs. Nerea de Clifford.
  Recorder and Archivist:
    Miss Gwen White.
  Council Members:
  Committee Members:
    Mrs. Wheatley.
    Mrs. Hope-Nicholson.
    Mrs. Wilbourne.
    Miss Fox-Hunter.
    Miss Fryer.
    Miss Blair Hickman.

Its objects are: —
  (a) *To ensure the preservation of old and interesting dolls, dolls' houses and accessories.*
  (b) *To encourage the production of good modern dolls, dolls' houses and accessories.*
  (c) *To raise money for recognised charities.*

by organising exhibitions, displays and competitions of dolls, with lectures and discussion groups.

They have a dolls' Newspaper and a Golden Book of beautiful dolls, which is a record of every lovely doll known to members, and which will soon include several dolls' houses as well.

They have dolls' dressmakers, who will create models, repair old garments, or make dresses from customers' own materials.

If you are fond of dolls, if you are interested in fashion, or if you like dolls' houses and their furnishings, you should join the Doll Club.

Annual subscription of 5/- for a full member, 2/6 for an Associate, and 6d. for a Junior under 17 years of age.

There are, at present, three *Recognised Branches* of the Doll Club: South Wales, Sussex and Lakeland.

The Doll Club is run for Collectors *and* "all people interested in all aspects" of dolls.

The Club has a collection of dolls, including a set of "Kings and Queens of England".

The Doll Club's bulletin is entitled *Plangon*. Edited by the Hon. Secretary, this useful news-sheet appears periodically and is circulated to Members. It records Club activities, information about Doll Exhibitions and carries an extensive "For Sale" and "Wanted" column.

It also announces the Rules for the Terrot Challenge Cup awarded annually for the doll which is judged to be the best-dressed doll costumed during the last 25 years. Pointers for this contest are : —

Entries must be dolls either owned or dressed by a member of the Doll Club. Entries must not have been entered in any other competition.

Entries must be not less than 3" or more than 3' in length. The dolls may be of any kind.

The clothing must have been made within twenty-five years of the year of the competition.

The costume may be of any kind, but in the event of a tie, the Cup will be awarded to a costume which could be worn today, rather than to a copy of an old dress.

Points are awarded for: —

(1) General appearance, proportion and beauty of the entry.
(2) Fine needlework.
(3) Originality.

The Club either organises or supports Exhibitions held in aid of divers charities. Every one of its members, male or female, are doll collectors. The Hon. Secretary is in regular touch with members in every part of the United Kingdom and is always willing to give information to interested people who write in the first place.

THE DOLLMAKERS' CIRCLE
THE HON. SECRETARY, MISS F. EATON,
16 CLIFTON GARDENS, LONDON, W.9.

was formed in 1957 by eight members of THE DOLL CLUB OF GREAT BRITAIN who were all greatly interested in designing and creating entirely hand-made dolls.

It is now planned to include dollmakers and those interested in dolls, here and abroad, with: —

Full membership for doll designers wishing to exhibit: —

Annual subscription (due in January) ... 15/-.

Associate membership for non-exhibitors who are interested in the News-sheet and activities: —

Annual subscription (due in January ... 7/-.

The AIMS of THE DOLLMAKERS' CIRCLE are: —

To discover and link individual dollmakers, by a News-sheet sent out three times a year.

To record and give information about dollmaking and dollmakers.

To arrange Exhibitions of members' work.

To promote interest, and good workmanship in dollmaking.

To hold periodic Meetings, at which a lecture, demonstration or display will be given.

The Dollmakers' Circle News-sheet, is published three or
four times annually. It circulates to Members and Associates
and carries articles of interest to makers; news of forthcoming
events; members' activities; correspondence; "For Sale" and
"Wanted" insertions; book reviews, etc.

Members meet socially twice a year for a Tea Party, at
which either a Lecture or an Exhibition (film-show, puppet
theatre, etc.), is given. This function enables them to make
new acquaintances, exchange doll news, and plan further
Exhibitions for Charity, which is a cardinal principle of its
membership.

Special Exhibitions

Many collectors and some museums arrange loan exhibits
in aid of good causes, charities, etc., and over the past ten
year successful Exhibitions have helped to raise such funds in
all the regions of the United Kingdom.

Owing to the lack of any Archive, or other recording system
in this country, no definitive checklist is available. Often
local newspapers report the occasion, but research workers,
as an expedient, are best advised to contact members of the
Dollmakers' Circle and the Doll Club of Great Britain, who
will be found to be well informed on Exhibitions held in
their respective districts.

* * *

A random list of only some of the special collections
mounted in recent years, here follows. It gives some impression of the scope of these events.

Exhibition of Character Dolls, created and loaned by Mrs. Widdows, of Birkdale, Lancashire, in aid of the N.S.P.C.C. (Westminster, London); 1952, Preston Town Hall (Save the Children Fund), etc.; and continually on view in various centres. For information and descriptive leaflets apply Mrs. Widdows, 8 Lancaster Road, Birkdale, Lancs.

Boutique Fantasque (1954), *Easter Eggs from Many Lands* (1962), etc., at 94 Wimpole Street, W.1, mounted by Paul and Marjorie Abbatt. (Souvenir programmes issued.)

Exhibition of Period Dolls, in aid of the Red Cross, mounted by Gordon Hand at 170 Kensington Church Street, London.

Period Dolls' Houses from Many Lands; Christmas, 1955, presented by the House of Bewlay for The Children's Aid Society. (Special souvenir catalogue.)

Costume Dolls and Figurines. An Exhibition of English Children's Costume Changes from ancient to contemporary, mounted by Mrs. Mildred Oversby for the Liverpool Museum (Lower Horseshoe Gallery), 1956. (Catalogue.)

Dolls Throughout the Ages; Exhibition, August, 1959, mounted by Faith Eaton, in aid of the Greater London Fund for the Blind, at the Tea Centre, Piccadilly, London; included a doll lent by Her Majesty the Queen. (Souvenir catalogue issued.)

A Pageant of Toys and Dolls, at The Shipley Gallery; including British, Continental and Far Eastern XIX century examples, lent by Mrs. Helena Clark, and period costume dolls made by the Townswomen's Guild of Gateshead.

Playthings Through the Ages. Exhibition, November, 1957, in aid of the Royal School for the Blind, Leatherhead; mounted by The House of Bewlay and opened by Mrs. Odette Hallowes, G.C., M.B.E., Legion d'Honneur. (Descriptive sheet issued.)

Exhibition of Applique and Embroidery Dolls by Lydia Fraser, May, 1958, at 24 Westbourne Park Road, W.2.

Children's Paradise. Exhibition of Playthings Through the Ages, 1957/Christmas, 1958, at The House of Bewlay, 138 Park Lane, London, in aid of Royal School for the Blind. (Catalogues issued.)

Doll Fashions Yesterday and Today, September-October, 1959. Anniversary Exhibition at Chiesman's of Lewisham, S.E.15, mounted by the Toy Museum.

Exhibition of Dolls and Dolls' Houses, Past and Present, March/April, 1959, at 21 Paulton's Square, S.W.3, mounted by Mrs. I. Spenser-Smith.

The Lakeland Festival of Dolls and Antiques; June, 1961, in aid of Dr. Barnardo's Homes, at The Methodist Hall, Millans Park, Ambleside; opened by Mr. Lewis Sorensen. (Illustrated handbill.)

M.P.M.A. Exhibition of Optical Toys, Magic Lanterns, Moving Picture Apparatus, Chromatropes, Slides, etc., at Qantas Gallery, Piccadilly, July, 1961. (Souvenir catalogue.)

Exhibition of Dolls and Books About Dolls, 1962, at The Mary Glasgow Bookshop, Earls Court Road, London, W.8.

Exhibition of Handmade Toys, September, 1962, mounted by the British Toymakers' Guild at Foyle's Art Gallery, W.C.2. (Leaflets issued.)

Changing Exhibitions of Toys, Toy Theatres, Runcible Cats, etc., at Pollock's Shop, 44 Monmouth Street, W.C.2. (Leaflets issued.)

Peggy Nisbet Costume and Portrait Dolls, at Peggy Nisbet, Ltd. (Catalogue.)

Dolls of Yesterday, Today and Tomorrow. Dolls—dating from 1800, of wood and wax, Victorian bisque and china, to modern ones designed and created by artist dollmakers, together with hand-made models of an Elizabethan dolls' house, gypsy caravan and a merry-go-round. Exhibited by Joan Cope and Faith Eaton, members of the Dollmakers' Circle and the Doll Club of Great Britain, at Birmingham & Midland Institute, January, 1962.

PART III
PRIVATE COLLECTIONS

ABOUT PRIVATE COLLECTIONS.

Private Collections in Britain and Ireland are numerous and it would be both undesirable and totally impracticable to publish a definitive list as is frequently done in the United States. There the prevalent climate among collectors favours more sociable and often gregarious activity, and a wide degree of give-and-take in expertise, visits and return visits, and so on, obtain through Toy Collectors' Clubs and Doll Collectors' Societies and Groups. These groups publish their own periodicals, which serve to keep enthusiasts well informed about what their rivals and fellow-members are doing.

In Britain we are more conservative about sharing our hoards. Here, a private collector tends to value, above all else, his *privacy*. This, of course, like a home or one's family life, is a highly personal matter and must always be respected by the student or enthusiast, however ardent his devotion to fieldwork may be.

There are, nevertheless, known personally to me, many collectors whose treasures I have enjoyed as an invited guest to their houses, workshops or studios. They are remarkable in generosity and in that they are willing, *on occasion,* to make other toy collectors welcome. They seem to be always ready to find time to accommodate serious students who are either working on a thesis or who hope to write, or illustrate, yet another book! Among these acceptable "intrusions" are numbered visits from oversea collectors; teachers and educationalists; designers and authors; journalists looking for a topical story around Christmas time for the local newspaper. Their patience is classic.

I have made it a strict rule that nobody's name and private address will appear in this Section, or any other Section of our Guide, without the owner's knowledge and consent—unless it be in instances where names are elsewhere already in print.

In special circumstances where readers particularly would like to meet a collector and inspect his or her collection, it goes without saying that the courtesy is essential to write first requesting an appointment. As has already been mentioned, domestic-based toy collections are often kept in a living-room or some other place used for family life. Whenever this is found to be the case, visitors who are professionally and vocationally interested in our fields, are reminded to respect to the full any privileges thus granted and that when they discuss the matter with friends or other interested parties, to stress that they have been to view a private and not a public exhibition.

Private Collectors—even the most withdrawn or sinister!—are usually known to Museum Curators near where they reside. Any of the Museums discussed elsewhere in these pages are all sources of helpful advice and, provided the visitor makes his/her business quite clear, and presents *bona fide* evidence of his/her motives, it is more likely than not that an introduction may be effected.

MISS FAITH EATON, 16 Clifton Gardens, London, W.9, collects antique dolls. Her collection grows continually and includes one of the earliest wax genuine "baby" dolls extant; some fine examples of wax sleeping dolls, wire-and-balance type; spinet dancing-dolls; a series of American dolls from early bisque to last composition; an English "pot" doll of 1918; and European Fashion Dolls of all periods.

Her foreign examples include 50 different *Kokeshi* (wooden folkdolls) from Japan, previously part of the Sir Edward Crowe Collection that was sold to Messrs. Hamley's and earned considerable funds for charitable causes. The traditional Japanese prototypes include paper dolls; Ukiyo-ningyo (Costume Dolls); Dairi-bina (Exalted Personages); Sakuraningo (Ornamental dolls); Samurai (Warrior Dolls); and Yamato-Ningyo (Playdolls) such as are displayed annually at Japanese Doll Festivals for Girls in Japan every spring. Miss Eaton arranged such a display at her home, as a Dollmakers'

Circle Tea-party in 1963, and the dolls were featured on B.B.C. Television. The film of the occasion is now in her possession.

She has many interesting examples of dolls made from natural materials—e.g., straw, corn-husk, gourds, coconut-fibre, latex, bread, apples and other edible confections. Her section of miniature dolls is mainly of wooden examples, all under 5″ high. In this category Miss Eaton collects miniature dolls' clothing and accessories; miniature newspapers; cut-outs, etc.

Juvenile postcards, scraps and scrapbooks, children's story books, nearly 200 colour slides about dolls, and films on kindred subjects all cause the collection to expand from year to year.

As a dollmaker she is best known for her original series of Character Dolls, "Cries of London". A set of these has recently been ordered for permanent exhibition at London Museum, and a descriptive article, supported by colour photographs, appears in the *Illustrated London News*, Special Christmas Number, 1963.

In his charming Elizabethan residence, Leydon House, at Mortlake, situated on the south bank of the Thames at the very spot where the Boat Race ends, the late Maurice Cockin lived with his treasured collection of African arts and crafts—fabulous Benin bronzes and Nigerian masks in the attic, and native carved dolls and toys in the drawing room.

A great collector, he evolved the charming hobby when travelling far and wide with his wife of buying traditional toys typical of every country they visited as presents for the children. Most of these entertaining playthings—the jumping-jacks, the Scandinavian horses, the clockwork animals—became part and parcel of the house's old world nursery, with its atmosphere recalling the time of John Dee and the Shakespearean dramatists.

When "the children got married and went away", Mr. Cockin removed the toys and set them out on the huge polished table in the drawing room with its heavy doors and panelled walls. Here, month after month, in the deserted room, they were left in perfect stillness—relics of the great happiness they had brought, symbols of the laughter of children who had flown from the nest.... But the toys were kept for a wonderful purpose. They were kept dusted and in good repair. Every Christmas Eve Mr. Cockin, who was adored by the local "village children" as he called them, threw open the doors of Leydon House to the junior population of Mortlake. Accompanied by parents and older sisters, they filed in rapt wonderment past the curtains and tapestries into the drawing room. The room had been transformed into a child's idea of Fairyland. Bright with flickering candles, there stood the toys! For all to crowd around the antique table and actually play with them....! Those few of us of an older generation privileged to have been invited to "peep in", must always remember the beaming face of the tall, handsome, white-haired traveller as he watched his young guests having fun with a hundred toys of yesteryear ... while the music-box tinkled sweetly in the candle-lit chamber, full of memories.

With his death in 1961 and the subsequenet sale of Leydon House, the toys fortunately were not disbanded. They passed on to his married daughter, MRS. CELIA GORDON BARCLAY, who holds for them as warm a regard and affection as did her parent.

Today the Cockin Collection of Toys from Many Lands is housed in her sitting room at "Wildwoods", Woodgreen Road, Waltham Abbey, Essex. Already they have been classified and rearranged and Exhibited in aid of the N.S.P.C.C. It is Mrs. Barclay's intention of setting up a tiny "museum" as an annexe to her house so that many more visitors may view the collection and make a small donation to a good cause like the "Freedom From Hunger" campaign, as a memorial to Maurice Cockin's life's work.

Many of the dolls are definitely "collector's pieces" and have never filled a child's Christmas stocking.

One huge glass cabinet in Mrs. Barclay's sitting room holds a collection of more than 100 Japanese, Chinese, and Burmese "figures".

Another cabinet is devoted to Indian and West African dolls—including many examples of exquisite native carvings.

In contrast, and more popular with Mrs. Barclay's young son, Toby, is the display of lead soldiers and constructed scenes of bullfights and fox hunting.

Mrs. Barclay is always willing to lend the dolls to local schools for educational purposes. Perhaps the most popular in this field is a set of Victorian dolls dressed in period costumes.

They trace the history of English dress from Saxon times, via the Tudor and Hanoverian periods to the "present day"— in this case late 19th century.

MRS. HELENA H. CLARK, Aldham House, Ryton-on-Tyne, County Durham, collects wooden toys of all periods and countries and has an especially fine assortment of peasant hand-made toys and figures from the fairy-tale village of Seiffen in Saxony, where she is a popular visitor and on whose village crafts and the traditional art of toy making she gives lectures to interested groups all over Britain from Tyneside in the North to Hampstead and Hastings in the South.

She illustrates her talks with examples of the Seiffen playthings packed in a handy suitcase.

Mrs. Clark is a lecturer on botany in the Department of Agriculture at King's College, Newcastle, but her hobby began when she spent a year as a student in Freiberg, in Saxony, which is near the famous toy-making village of Seiffen, reputed to be the place where the story of Snow White and the Seven Dwarfs originated.

Mrs. Clark tells how all the people in the village worked in the silver mines in the mountains surrounding Seiffen until the ore ran out about 200 years ago.

Then, rather than leave their village, they looked around

for some other means of livelihood and found it in the forests that surrounded the village and their own skill as craftsmen. Using the many different types of wood, they started carving the toys which are now world famous and many of which are in the same traditional designs as the first toys.

Mrs. Clark's friends in Saxony regularly send her different toys to add to her collection.

MR. ROBERT CULFE, 38 Islington Park Street, N.1, is an author who has become an enthusiastic toy collector. The object of forming the Culfe Collection of Antique Toys to bring together a representative group of toys likely to be found in the nurseries of nineteenth and early twentieth century children. The items are arranged under several headings: Dolls and Dolls' Houses; Games and Puzzles; Card Games and Paper Toys; Books; Playthings; Juvenile Drama Sheets and Toy Theatres. Among the two hundred and fifty-odd items there are a number of very rare and interesting old toys. The three dolls' houses are outstandingly well appointed and arranged, two of them being early nineteenth century; they house a group of Regency *papier mâché* and wooden "Dutch" dolls among furnishings of the same period. In the doll section is a well-preserved Montanari wax doll from the Martineau family, a unique rag Mammy doll of about 1840, and as a representative of the 1890s a wax doll made by the Pierrotti brothers, the last of the great English wax-doll craftsmen.

The collection is particularly rich in its Juvenile Drama section; characters and scenes from the English Toy Theatre range from the early nineteenth century sheets of West, Hodgson and Dyer, through the 1d. and ½d. publishers, down to the original drawings executed by Robert Culfe himself for a play published in the 1950s by Benjamin Pollock Ltd., "The Flying Saucerers". In the Playthings section are many unusual toys: A Noah's Ark (C1850) with interior stalls and ladders; German tin clockwork toys; some of them with their original boxes, and one in the form of a clown who can draw

PLATE XIV

[*Photo, Irish Tourist Board*

The Chapel of Titania's Palace. (*See pp.* 85-88)

PLATE XV

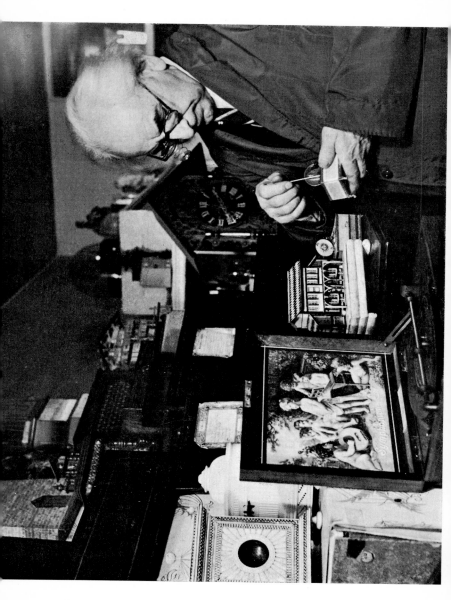

Bernard Sunley with some of his treasures. (See pp. 168-172)

From the Pinto Collection (See pp. 46-47)

PLATE XIX

The Batty Dolls' House (See pp. 82-85)

[*Photos, G. R. Erwood*]

PLATE XX

Plate XXI

The Batty Dolls' House (See pp. 82-85)

[*Photos, G. R. Erwood*]

Plate XXII

PLATE XXIII

Dutch Dolls from the Collection of W. S. Lanchester (See p. 217)

PLATE XXIV

Anna Marita (See p. 138)

[B.T.H.A. Photo]

PLATE XXV

Britain's First Puppet Theatre. (See p. 129)

a portrait of Queen Victoria; an Erzgebirge model village and other wooden toys of the 19th century.

The collection of Antique Toys has appeared in programmes on television; items from it have been lent to libraries and in aid of various charities; and part is on loan to Pollock's of Monmouth Street.

The collection was on Exhibition at Stepney Central Library, E.1, in November, 1960, entitled "150 Years of Children's Toys".

Mrs. Joan Cope, 84 High Street, Broadway, Worcestershire (where she also runs "The Dolls' House" toyshop), has in her collection of dolls a large number of wooden, wax, *papier mâché*, bisque, composition and leather specimens.

Among the more interesting are an old wooden doll in original clothes, early 19th century; a wax doll from John Ruskin's collection (he is said to have had at least 200 dolls); an 1850 Pedlar doll; a wax doll whose eyes open and close by means of a wire in her side, and a Blue Scarf doll. The latter was given to a little girl in the 1870s, and she died recently aged nearly 90. Such dolls are rare; it has a sawdust body and a lovely head. A wax Shrine doll came from Belgium, and a wooden doll with a stiff dress of cardboard covered with small stones or sand, is thought to be a type of shell doll made in Victorian days.

Dolls'-house dolls of all types and ages, include one early Victorian in wood, dressed in velvet cloak with pointed cap. There is also a dolls' house—hand-made model of an Elizabethan house—with period furniture; an inlaid, hooded doll cradle, about 1800, and a Jacobean baby's' cradle; an interesting child's rocking chair; solid wooden sides, and a miniature one for her doll. Period doll chairs and an upholstered doll's Victorian sofa of the 1850s.

The collection includes several Nun dolls, one with a small prayer book with prayers written in French, one of the last Cobo Sally dolls made in Guernsey. These are so tightly stuffed they weigh 1½ lbs.! Many bisque dolls; Russian dolls dating from 1920s, Frozen Charlottes and Penny Woodens are also here.

Included in the Victorian children's games are Dissected Maps and Noah's Ark jig-saws; Thames Tunnel Peepshow; Floral Lotto; Game of Schimmel; numerous card games and a set of Table Croquet similar to one illustrated in *Country Life* (1960); and the game of Pope Joan. Another box contains a set of circular cards with letters of the alphabet, and a box of dominoes carved from meat bones by prisoners of the Napoleonic wars is of interest.

Most of Mrs. Cope's children's books belonged to relations, e.g., *An Illustrated Book of Nursery Rhymes and Song and Music, A Book of Drolleries, Evening Amusement, Silhouettes of 1872, Mrs. Prentiss's Little Lou, How Patty Learned Her Alphabet,* and some of Kate Greenaway's books. Peter Parley stories dating from 1850. Illustrated copy of *Precocious Piggy; Girl's Own Toymaker; Beaumont's Strange Adventure of a Toy Soldier; Memoirs of a London Doll,* and three Scrapbooks made in the 1870s.

Perhaps the most spectacular toy is the 2' 6" model of a gypsy caravan, complete with furnishings and skin horse, hand-made. Others are mechanical lambs; a 1910 Teddy Bear; Cup and Ball game; 1909 child's sewing machine; toys of tin; set of Punch and Judy puppet characters, with hand-carved heads.

Her modest library gives plenty of scope for research, as it includes most of the English and American books about dolls and dolls' houses, as well as books about Toys, Games and Costume.

MARGARET HUTCHINGS, The Manor House, Ongar, Essex, is always pleased to welcome visitors, especially children and folk from overseas to her tiny workroom. The toys and dolls piled high in the cupboards, about 500 of them, are not for sale but are mostly the original models used in the six books she has so far written and in her television demonstrations and magazine and newspaper articles.

Among the most interesting are perhaps, her miniature shops, Christmas Crib figures, rag dolls, hobby-horses and her collection of Patchwork Playthings which is probably unique.

Visitors will also find a family of Golliwogs ranging from 18" to $\frac{1}{2}$" high, and every conceivable kind of animal, both real and imaginary!

She has appeared several times on TV with her toys and won at various times most of the major awards for toy making.

Her work used to be mostly done in a most beautiful old painted gypsy caravan standing under a centuries-old cedar tree by the Anglo-Saxon mound at the foot of her garden, but now finds she needs more space and delights in a specially built new workroom.

Miss W. Elaine Johnson, "Wyndor", 13 Hillside, Banstead, Surrey, collects Costume Dolls which, being a teacher, she utilises for lecturing on "History Through Costume". Her fascinating talks appeal to pupils because illustrated by more than 100 dolls authentically dressed in period styles from 1066-1900. Each doll represents a change in fashion—the largest being only 6" tall. Miss Johnson arranges to visit other schools or adult groups.

The Lilian Lunn Collection of 170 dolls, made entirely in crochet-work (silk and cotton), will be known to a large section of the public from its tour of cities such as Manchester, Liverpool, Leicester, Derby, Birmingham, Bolton, Salford, Wigan (Haigh Hall), Halifax, York (Castle Museum) and London.

The immediate charm which these figures have is the result of six years' hard work and experiment. Twisted wools, velvet cords, and threads are worked with needle and crochet-hook until the foundation is complete, and on this the features, ornaments, flowers and other decorations are worked with fine silk threads.

Although most of the figures are designed after contemporary portraits of particular individuals, they aim at a truthful impression of the costume style of a period rather than a

realistic reconstruction in miniature. By respecting the limi-
tations and exploiting the possibilities of her medium Mrs.
Lunn has succeeded in giving impressionistic truth to these
very charming creations.

Lilian Lunn, a native of Buxton, has written a fully descriptive Catalogue which is obtainable at travelling Exhibitions.

ADMIRAL SIR MICHAEL DENNY, formerly C.-in-C. Home Fleet,
collects Tourist Costume Dolls—souvenirs of the many ports
he has visited during his naval service. Before his retirement
Sir Michael displayed his collection aboard the flagship,
Apollo—photographed in *The Daily Mail*.

MR. COOPER, The Beach Club, Peacehaven, Sussex, has a
fine collection of miniature wagons, the majority being scale
models but some being toys. (Models of horse-omnibuses
which plied the streets in the second half of the last century
are on public view at London's Museum of Transport.)
are on public view at London's Museum of Transport, Clap-
ham.)

MR. ROLAND KNASTER, 12 Kingston House, South London,
S.W.7, has a superb collection in store—since it has grown too
large for accommodation in his flat. It consists largely of
papiers de fantasie; paper toys and cut-out books; scraps,
greeting cards and playing cards; penny-plains and tinsel
pictures; peepshows; toybooks and panoramic or fold-up picture books; children's early school stationery and copybooks,
writing, exercises, alphabets, counting games, hornbooks, etc.
The bulk of the collection consists of children's story books
and picture books, many of them rare and of mint quality.

MR. PETER OPIE, Westerfield House, West Liss, Hants, an
authority on Nursery literature, collects children's books,
illustrated 18th century juvenile texts of moral import; and,
of course, Nursery Rhyme editions of every type. He has
lately added period dolls to his and his wife's collecting
interests.

MR. BERNARD HINCHLEY, 68 Marlborough Road, Watford,
Herts., is a specialist in toy and model trains. He is adviser

to The Toy Museum in this field and has a private collection of early specimens of locomotives, rolling stock, tracks and station equipment and line accessories.

THE RAYMOND BARNETT COLLECTION of Toy Theatres and miscellaneous toys has been presented to the Victoria and Albert Museum. (*See page* 16).

MR. R. ANTHONY MICHAELIS, 7 Hanover Terrace, Regents Park, N.W.1, has an interesting collection of pre-cinema optical toys ranging from static magic lantern slides and chromatropes to apparatus such as the Zoëtrope, Thaumatrope, and Phenakistiscope. He also collects weights and measures from all parts of the world.

MR. HERMANN HECHT, 15 New Road, London, W.C.2, is an authority on lantern slides (moving and static) and has assembled a valuable amount of data concerning these for a prospective book on the subject.

MR. R. G. RIRLEW, a bank manager at Brighton, has a collection of money-boxes (known to American collectors as money-banks or piggy-banks) totalling over 100.

MRS. ILSA ERLANGER, 89 St. Mary Abbotts Court, Earl's Court, S.W.5, collects dolls of every kind.

MR. PERCY MUIR, Takeley, nr. Bishops Stortford, Herts., has a mixed collection of Victorian toys—with special reference to "geographical" and "instructional" table-games; a unique Easter-bunny automaton; musical boxes, toybooks and peepshows and, of course, rare editions of children's books on which he is an authority. Mr. Muir is, also, author of *English Children's Books*, 1600-1900. (Batsford.)

THE MAJOR F. R. B. WHITEHOUSE COLLECTION of Board Games and Table Games (on which an illustrated catalogue was privately published in 1951). For particulars as to its present location, communicate with the Managing Director, Messrs. Chad Valley Co. Ltd., Harborne, Birmingham, 17.

MRS. RICHARD BARTON, Annamoe, Co. Wicklow, Ireland, has a collection of primitive dolls and toys, from South American Indian, and ancient Aztec origin; also ornamental objects and terracottas of magico-religious interest.

Mr. Ronald Horton, 47 Brangwyn Drive, Withdean, Brighton, Sussex, is a collector of children's books and allied juvenilia. He also has peepshows; folding alphabets; Wallis instructional games of wide variety; Juvenile Drama sheets; cut-out sheets; and novelty sheets of period interest. He paints pictures of toys and, being primarily concerned with arts and crafts as a teacher and lecturer, he has built up an impressive collection of graphic material on toys, including an archive of black-and-white and colour slides. Many of the latter are of toys made by pupils in craft classes.

Mrs. Irene Barton, 4 York Mansions, Prince of Wales Drive, Battersea Park, S.W., collects dolls; 18th century juvenilia like hand-painted prints, broadsheets and children's books; toy theatre material; miscellaneous games and toys.

Miss Marjorie Parkes, of Purley, Surrey, has a remarkable collection of period dolls; souvenir and costume dolls from many countries, and is a keen member of The Doll Club of Great Britain.

Mrs. Widdows, Birkdale, Lancs., makes and collects Character Dolls. These comprise Historical, National, Literary and Nursery groups, with which she tours in aid of charities. Recently Mrs. Widdows has given lecture-demonstrations with these toys in foreign countries, sponsored by the British Council.

Mrs. D. Masterman, 7 Hanover Terrace, N.W.1, collects hand-painted scraps and scrapbooks; all varieties of print and juvenile print; children's books and annuals; miscellaneous graphic items, and being an illustrator of children's books, etc., is especially interested in book design.

Miss Joyce Holt, 3 Summerhow Cottages, Shap Road, Kendal, Westmorland, has a representative collection of folk-toys and children's books.*

* For illustrations see *Children's Toys Throughout the Ages* (Daiken) ("Some Toy Collections", Page 188).

MADAME F. FASTRÉ, Kimberley Cottage, Dean Way, Chalfont St. Giles, Bucks., is a retired Belgian opera singer who has assembled a remarkable collection of toys and dolls. These are specially housed in quarters near her residence. Appointments are usually made through her Secretary.

MISS BARBARA JONES, 2 Well Walk, Hampstead, N.W.3, collects bizarre bric-a-brac, machinery, juvenilia and domestic appliances of all kinds. A specialist in *Victoriana*, Miss Jones is interested in popular art and her concern with toys, games, lantern slides, scrapbooks, peepshows, panoramic books, postcards, and kindred items, comes within these terms of reference.

MR. WEBB, 53 Avenue Gardens, Acton, W.3, has a representative collection of peepshows, early children's editions, paper novelties, etc.

MRS. NEREA DE CLIFFORD, 12 The Close, New Malden, Surrey, has a very fine doll collection, specialising in 18th century playdolls. She is also a collector of witchcraft dolls of which she has many hair-raising tales to tell. Among her more unusual Costume Dolls is a series illustrating the history of Nuns' habits representative of many religious orders. Hon. Secretary of The Doll Club of Great Britain, Mrs. de Clifford is in touch with all its individual members, is familiar with their respective collections and is always willing to put members in touch with others having similar interests.

MR. AND MRS. SIMES, 80 Colherne Court, Old Brompton Road, London, S.W., collects wooden bygones, with an emphasis on mechanical objects, among which are many toys of movement made from bone-ivory by Napoleonic prisoners-of-war detained in England.

Doll Collecting is not necessarily a hobby or passion for people of maturer age. It may begin, consciously, in childhood. An interesting instance of this is Shenagh Hennessy aged 11, who was inspired by her mother's doll collecting, to begin on her own. Shenagh has written the story of how the "collecting craze" began, specially for readers of this *Guide*

MY COLLECTION OF DOLLS

By SHENAGH HENNESSY

I went to Cyprus when I was three years old and was given my first costume dolls. They are a man and woman in Greek dress and I called them Maru and Andreas. Later, I was sent a doll from Canada; she is dressed entirely in white leather and beadwork, done by the Indian tribe in 1948. My Godmother sent me a doll from Mexico, made from a corn husk. It has no arms or legs and is dressed in brightly coloured cotton.

After two years in Cyprus we returned to England. Our first holiday was in Ireland, where I bought an Irish colleen doll. Someone gave me a Bog Oak cauldron in a tripod and I put this with the doll when on show. We drove back through Wales, where I was given a doll in Welsh costume; it even has a miniature leek brooch.

Our next stay abroad was Aden, and on our way by boat we stopped at Port Said. Daddy bought me a small leather camel with an Arab doll seated on its back. It is most unusual to see an Arab doll, as they don't like images. The shops in Aden have many dolls of other countries though, for many Asian people live there, including Indian, Chinese and Somali. As we were there for two years I added many dolls to my collection. I have two which are supposed to be Hindu gods, Rahda and Khristna. Khristna is pale blue and plays a pipe; Rahda is in a beautiful sari.

I bought several Japanese dolls. My favourite is wearing a kimono, and a flat hat and she carries a branch of wisteria. She has a china face and inset eyes. There are a lot of these shops in Aden and there we could buy a variety of. I have one in red brocade with pig-tails, another is a which has a small baby doll strapped on her back. a little rag doll and a great favourite of mine. He to be a Chinese coolie wearing a blue cotton suit and hat like a cone. I also have two very tiny Chinese ich are embroidered in gold; the lady has a dragon

111

on her tunic, and long fingernails.

Mummy bought me a Greek doll in Adane, she is elaborately dressed in silk with gold sequins on her dress and gold coins round her neck. She carries a basket on her head with fruit in.

From Aden we flew to Kenya for a holiday and there I discovered my most unusual doll, she is wearing Purdah; that is a black silk cloak with a net square over the face. Underneath she wears an Indian dress, for many of the Indian ladies in Mombasa are still in Purdah. From Kenya also came my African doll, a mother with a baby on her back and a bundle of sticks on her head. It's quite usual to see the East African native women like this.

When the two years were up, we returned to England, again by boat, and I acquired a sailor doll on the boat with the name "R.M.S. Cillicia" on its hat band. We stopped at Port Suez and we went to Cairo to see the Pyramids. We bought an Egyptian doll before we went back to the boat; it is dressed in black and green and has gold earrings.

All my other dolls I have bought in England, but an aunt sent me a lovely Spanish dancer from Lisbon and two small Portuguese dolls, made entirely of wool; one is spinning and the other is using a flale.

I hope I shall travel to other places one day, where I can find some new dolls for my collection; but Mummy is not sure where we can put them all.

(*Age* 11 *years.*)

In the nature of things, antique dolls and toys cannot be mass-produced just to satisfy the appetites of collectors. Most dealers, antique traders, old houses and junk shops have been thoroughly scoured by collectors and their agents, so that it is a rare occasion for an unknown collection or hoard to come to light. But Britain, having a rich history and its patterns of family life being more circumscribed than in say, the U.S.A. (despite new transatlantic trends and fashions), still hides a few secrets. When these are revealed by an accidental "find", the news creates excitement among collectors and usually makes good feature material in the illustrated magazines.

The following Note, published with excellent photographic support in *Country Life* (December 20th, 1962), is typical of such an occurrence: —

When, by chance, the fragile toys that delighted the childhood of our grandparents have survived, then the whole round world of those now far-off nurseries can be re-lived by us. It was a different world to this—serene, sometimes harsh, but full of a disciplined yet spontaneous enjoyment, and it was far less sophisticated.

It was my great good fortune recently to be presented with the contents of an old toy cupboard of vintage years, when a house of long occupancy changed hands. Pleasure gave place to astonishment at the toys' survival, and especially so because some were in ther original little boxes. How did it come to pass? I was told that they had served two generations of boys and girls, but were only dished out two at a time ten minutes before bedtime. By this means the children did not grow tired of them; although, as my informant pointed out, it did not account for the broken ones that passed into oblivion. Some are toys to be played with, and others come under the heading of parlour amusements; they date from the earliest period of the mechanical toy to the end of the last century. Some are German (curiously enough, both those that portray Queen Victoria), and some French and some characteristically English toys might have come directly out of Caleb Plummer's cracked nutshell of a wooden house, in Dickens's *Cricket on the Hearth*.

The amiable elephant, which is still in its box, bears the inscription: "With Aunt Hattie's love to Helen." Does that not convey something of the aura of the '70s, when on some snowy Christmas morning of long ago the elephant shuffled down a slope for the first time?

ALLAN JOBSON.

114

PART IV

ALL ABOUT PUPPETS, MARIONETTES, PUNCH-AND-JUDY MEN, JUVENILE DRAMA, THE MINIATURE THEATRE

(Contributed by JANE PHILLIPS, Hon. Editor of
The Puppet Master, organ of the B.P.M.T.G.P.)

It has been a real advantage in the writing and compilation of this book to bear in mind throughout that it would be of interest to the adult as well as the juvenile reader. Those of us who glibly remark "kid's stuff" while jealously preserving for our sophisticated pleasure some rare musical-box or set of Burmese marionettes are apt to forget that *Homo Ludens* gropes onwards, in stages, from the cradle to the grave. Among the toys most possessively appropriated by "Second Childhood", are the joys of marionettes.

There are two schools of thought among the puppetry people. The purists hold that this field belongs to adult theatre, should be occupied solely by professionals (or amateurs with a seriously adult dedication) and have no truck with children's interests. The more liberal puppeteers take the view that if puppet-play did not have an intrinsic appeal for juveniles—there would be no audiences! Moreover, that the toy trade, in present times, turns out and sells many more little glove and string puppets designed for children *to play with* (and thus grow into enthusiastic Puppet Masters!), than do craftsmen for the entire grown-up community.

Fortunately, both opinions are accepted as being right, in the context of this guidebook. The pedantic and elderly will, in their roles of parents, uncles and even grandparents, find plenty of information to strengthen their bias: while the younger people can absorb the same information from the sources mentioned, to enable them to argue profitably their case that the child is father to the man.

In the Ethnographic Department of the British Museum two sets of Asiatic rod-marionettes are exhibited. One series is Javanese, collected by Sir Stamford Raffles before 1817. It is made of buffalo-hide, intricately pierced and painted, and having finely-wrought handles of horn.

These puppets, from Wayang, were used to animate plays based on Hindu mythology. They were seen principally by adult audiences, performed after dark so that a lamp cast their shadows on a screen; but privileged young Chinese people did formerly participate, and now do so very much more often.

The main characters in the play cycle consist of Princes and Princesses; Servants and Warriors; Demons and figures grotesque and comical. The series here shown also include traditional weapons, manipulated like the shadow-puppets themselves, and an essential part of the dramatisations.

On the other side of the screen is presented a set of sixteen figures from Pekin. These are made of translucent skin parchment, and are used in shadow plays similarly to those from Java just described. The arms and legs are jointed but give a greater effect in action of naturalism. Their purpose is one of entertainment solely, and not a religious one, as in Java. The play themes are mythological, and performed to standard written texts. The characters in the collection here shown are: —A Wicked Counsellor; Kuan-Yu, a Hero of The Three Kingdoms; a Married Peasant Woman of South China; an Unmarried Manchu Girl; a Student Dressed for Leisure; Merchants; Clowns; Servants; Stilt Walkers; and a Horse Hauling a Load of Demons.

If you enjoy making puppets or seeing puppet shows, you might like to join a society interested in puppetry. There are three such societies in this country, the British Puppet and Model Theatre Guild, the Educational Puppetry Association, and UNIMA (Union Internationale des Marionettes). The EPA is interested in the teaching of puppetry and its uses outside the theatre, such as in schools and hospitals. UNIMA is an international puppetry association just starting up again now, after the war. It has members in 40 countries and forms a link between puppeteers throughout the world. Then there is the BPMTG. It is interested in encouraging the art of puppetry in all its forms, improving the standards of puppetry in this country and linking enthusiasts, both amateur and professional.

Our Guild was founded in 1925 by a few puppetomanes who wanted to keep alive the Juvenile Drama, i.e., the "penny plain and tuppence coloured" shows given by Georgian and Victorian children in their toy theatres. Also, these founders were artists who wanted to make model theatres and puppets. They began by meeting occasionally to talk and show one another their work. Then they organised Guild Exhibitions and published a newsletter for members. Membership grew by leaps and bounds when a revival of puppetry began in this country. The Guild played an important part in this revival. Many of our members wrote books on how to make and act with puppets and the first television puppet shows were given by our President, H. W. Whanslaw, in John Logie Baird's experimental studios. The popularity of puppets became so great that they became the main interest of the Guild and the model theatres became part of a general interest in puppetry of all kinds, including shadow puppets, rod puppets, marionettes, glove puppets and Punch & Judy shows. Eventually the use of puppetry in education grew and became so absorbing that some members branched out to form the EPA and specialize in this subject.

From the very beginning, the Guild has always been noted

for its friendly atmosphere. Among our members at home and abroad, some are amateur puppeteers, some are semi-professional, some professional and some just enjoy watching puppet shows. All are welcome. We have a Junior section but not as many young people as we should like to see, for in this stay-at-home age we have quite a difficult time to keep going. Television, which has brought fame and fortune to many puppets, now keeps a lot of people from attending our meetings and also the popularity of puppets has brought them sometimes into disrepute. Many people think having seen one puppet show and how it works, they have seen them all. It is now our task to reinstate puppets in the theatre and to prove that it is not how the puppets work that is important, but what you can say with them.

THE BRITISH PUPPET AND MODEL THEATRE GUILD

*Headquarters: 10 Draper's Gardens, London, E.C.2

President: H. W. WHANSLAW

Vice-Presidents:

Harold Aidalberry	John Carr, O.B.E.
Waldo Lanchester, F.R.S.A.	Oliver Haslam, F.R.S.A.
Cecil Stavordale	Edith Lanchester
Gerald Morice	Cecil Madden, M.B.E.
George Speaight	Percy Press
Charles Nicholson	Walter Wilkinson
	Harry Clarke

Chairman: PERCY PRESS (Primrose 2723)

Vice-Chairman: WILLIAM MEACOCK

Secretary: GORDON SHAPLEY

c/o Headquarters, B.P.M.T.G.

Treasurer: ERNEST SHUTT (Tate Gallery 4871)

7 Lupus Street, S.W.1

Registrar: MRS. SHUTT

* *See next page*

118

THE OBJECTS OF THE GUILD *(Founded in* 1925)

To encourage the Art and Practice of Puppetry in all its forms and to foster interest in the Model Theatre.

To improve the standards of Production and Performance.

To act as a channel of communication between **Puppetry** and Model Theatre enthusiasts everywhere, both Professional and Amateur.

The facilities offered to members include: —

The Monthly Newsletter and Quarterly Journal, *The Puppet Master,* both issued free to members. On sale to the public, 2/6 per issue.

The service of a panel of experts who will give advice on all aspects of puppetry.

Free use of the Guild Library.

Sales Section.

Frequent meetings for Discussion, Puppet Demonstrations and Lectures.

Participation in Exhibition and Festivals.

Membership is open to all who are in sympathy with the objects of the Guild. If you are a Puppeteer, amateur or professional, a Teacher, a Model Theatre Maker, or otherwise interested in Puppetry, you are eligible. Applications for membership are subject to the approval of the Council.

The Entrance Fee is 5/- in each case to cover the cost of registration, and the annual subscriptions are as follows:—

Adults ... ... 37/6.
Juniors ... ... £1 if under 18 and still at school.
Groups ... ... £5:5:0 for any number.
Family ... ... 50/- for two adults, plus 5/- for each child.

Subscriptions become due on 1st October each year, but new members joining after 1st April lay reduced subscriptions (Adults £1, Juniors 10/-s, Groups £2:12:6, Family £1:5:0 +2/6 each child and full entrance fee).

Application Forms for membership may be obtained from:—

GORDON SHAPLEY (*Hon. Secretary*),
16 Ashburn Place, London, S.W.7.

THE EDUCATIONAL PUPPETRY ASSOCIATION

This vigorous group has a special interest for teachers at all levels and, of course, for kindergarten parent-teacher and preschool playgroups.

The Secretary, 23a Southampton Place, Bloomsbury, W.C.2, will send full details, only do please enclose s.a.e.

During school terms their Headquarters are open to visitors from overseas, and other interested persons.

On Monday evenings at 6 p.m. the Association runs classes

in the making, manipulating and organising of puppetry; festivals; and participates in conferences and functions under similar auspices.

It has a well-stocked Library and publishes its own journal, *Puppet Post*.

EDUCATIONAL PUPPETRY

(Contributed by A. R. PHILPOTT, Editor of *Puppet Post*, journal of the E.P.A.)

Even those children who have learned how to handle a puppet themselves, to perform with puppets, still credit the puppets with a kind of "life" of their own. I think, too, that any genuine Puppeteer—especially if he or she makes his or her own puppets—has an affection for the puppets and knows that, during their periods on the stage (and the stage can be *anywhere*!) they are in fact being imbued with life through the Puppeteer.

Whether puppetry as a "school subject" will ever become "a compulsory subject" for teachers-in-training in this country—as it now is in Czechoslovakia, which is, incidentally, one of the "homes" of puppetry, with thousands of amateurs interested actively in the art, as well as its impressive professional companies, remains to be seen. Certainly, many training colleges have been taking an increasing interest in puppetry, with students producing excellent shows and testing it out in their school-practice periods. Some, alas, do *not* do it on the right lines and one unfortunately sees some of the "bad" results in the schools later. Puppetry *can* be just as much another school "chore" as any other subject done in an uninteresting way. There is still too much accent on the swotting up of puppet "history" and too little on the right understanding of puppetry as an activity and an art. Those who happen to see only the "bad" puppetry are quite right to question its value to the child and as a "teaching aid".

But I myself have seen shows *by* children—particularly by the junior age group—which I would cheerfully *pay* to see in preference to some "professional" shows. The shows may not quite amount to "art", but they have a vitality and an imaginative approach often sadly lacking in professional shows.

It is not the aim of the educationalists to produce a race of puppeteers—but just as it is recognised today that there is a natural and legitimate "child art" and "child drama" (nothing to do with forced forms imposed by adults) so there is also a natural (and therefore just as legitimate) "child puppetry". If you watch even very young children at play you can see them "puppetizing" everything they play with. To them not only live things (like their pets) have "life", can be played with and spoken to, but also their dolls and toys— and sometimes they even have "invisible playmates". In other words—as primitive peoples do—and children go through a primitive phase (try to remember your own childhood . . .)— children *animate* objects. Puppeteers animate puppets.... As a puppeteer I must acknowledge a debt to all the children I have had as audiences and have played with or simply spoken to outside the stage. One can learn enormously from them about the most effective things to put in plays.

UNION INTERNATIONALE DES MARIONETTES

This is a world organisation with member countries affiliated. Its present Headquarters are at Prague, Czechoslovakia, but up-to-date information, literature, terms of membership, news of puppet events in other countries, etc., may all be obtained from the United Kingdom national Secretary:—

C. M. MacDonald,
c/o 16 Ashburn Place, London, S.W.7.

THE MARIONETTE COMPANIES
(Contributed by George Speaight. (*See page* 140).)

Among English marionette companies now functioning the best-known names are those of the Lanchester Marionettes, the Hogarth Puppets directed by Jan Russell, and John

Wright's Marionettes, but there are perhaps a couple of dozen fully professional troupes, and several hundred semi-professional companies giving occasional performances.

Glove puppets and marionettes are by no means the only forms of puppetry. There are also rod puppets, controlled from under the stage, and shadow puppets. Happily, a few modest beginnings have been made towards creating permanent puppet theatres. At Stratford-upon-Avon the Lanchester Marionettes maintain a Puppet Centre, with a shop and a small display of historic figures; at Edinburgh the Lee Puppets have converted a mews into a small theatre, where they play regularly during the Festival and at other seasons; at Colwyn Bay Eric Bramall has created his permanent puppet theatre; in London the British Puppet and Model Theatre Giuld has obtained premises in the City as headquarters, with a small stage and auditorium, and John Wright an old temperance hall in Islington into a public marionette theatre.

In the midst of so many difficulties, the puppet has found one valuable ally in television. The small screen provides an almost ideal medium, and puppets appear regularly in the children's programmes, where such characters as Andy Pandy and Muffin the Mule have become household names. From time to time the television companies produce full-length puppet plays, and the B.B.C. has its own Television Puppet Theatre, with its own production under Gordon Murray.

Yet, valuable and welcome though this is, the puppet theatre, like any other kind of theatre, requires a living audience to bring it really alive. It is only when the little wooden actors can draw a response of laughter or wonder or tears from the people rapt in attention round them that their art is made truly manifest. When this is achieved the ancient magic surely works again.

FOUR PERMANENT THEATRES

(*Contributed by* G. L. SOMERVILLE.)

The Puppet Theatre has a distinguished past. It is one of the earliest forms of drama known to man and owes its beginnings more to the serious business of religion than to the entertainment of children as is usual today. Like all the best things in time, it has ended up in children's hands, and it is to be hoped that children will continue to enjoy seeing, and performing, puppet shows and thus keep the Puppet Theatre alive in this country.

I.—"THE LITTLE ANGEL." MARIONETTE THEATRE is London's only permanent Puppet Theatre.

If you are in the London area you would find it worthwhile to become a "Friend". It is the home of John Wright's well-known marionettes. Membership is only 5/-, puts you on the permanent mailing list, so that you receive advance notice of new productions, with priority for bookings, and lets you in on experimental shows and what John refers to as "various junketings".

The address is: 14 Dagmar Passage, Cross Street, Islington, N.1, and Cross Street is a bus stop for Nos. 38, 38a, 4, 19, 30, 171, 172, 73 and various other buses. Nearest Underground Station is the Angel (and the theatre is not far from the old Collins Music Hall). The premises are just back of St. Mary's Church, Upper Street. The telephone No.: CAN 1787.

Two main productions have been seen during the summer season—"Mak the Sheep Stealer" and "The Wild Night of the Witches". Oscar Wilde's "Salome" is in preparation. In addition there are variety items and some interesting experimental ones.

Saturday mornings have been given over to Glove Puppet shows — provided by EPA Members — and have proved popular, as have Saturday afternoon matinees for children.

John Wright is now a member of EPA Joint International Committee—his puppets are much-travelled.

Special terms are given for block bookings and many school

parties have visited the theatre.

II.—THE LANCHESTER MARIONETTES have their headquarters at 39 Henley Street, Stratford-on-Avon ('phone 3774), and are the creation of Waldo and Muriel Lanchester, the latter now enjoying the distinction of being one of the oldest members of the B.P.M.T.G.

They have experienced more than twenty-five years of travelling round Britain, during which time they have given over 5,000 performances and travelled 150,000 miles by road. They have been to Scotland fifteen times, and travelled into Wales many times, and have visited Northern Ireland.

The present Puppet Centre at Stratford started in London in 1927 as the Lanchester Marionette Theatre.

It was then a hobby, with a few twelve-men Marionettes, and for three years performances were given to audiences gathered together by invitation. In 1930 the present troupe of Marionettes, half as large again as the old ones, was started, and from then until today the troupe has been added to continuously. It was in 1936 that the Lanchester Marionette Theatre opened in permanent premises in Malvern as a part or an added attraction to the existing Malvern Drama Festival. Sir Barry Jackson, director of the Festival at that time, honoured them by opening their little Theatre and George Bernard Shaw was among the audience.

During the Drama Festivals the Marionettes played three times daily to packed houses for the whole of the period, which lasted a month. It was from these shows that the Lanchesters got bookings all over the country, for private parties of all kinds, Schools and Colleges and Dramatic Societies. This was the beginning of their travelling outfit.

At the Paris Exhibition of 1937, Puppet Companies from all over Europe were invited to give performances at a Theatre in the Exhibition, the Lanchester Marionettes were one of the three companies to go from this country, and they gave five performances.

The Lanchesters were privileged to perform at Buckingham

Palace before Queen Mary, Their Majesties, the Princesses and guests on December 14th, 1938.

The Marionette Theatre in Malvern was quite a small affair, with only fifty seats, and it was opened periodically, mostly at Easter, Whitsun and Christmas, and of course during the summer, when the Festivals were held. During the war no Festivals took place, but the Marionettes still gave their Summer Seasons. At the start the small Theatre was not always filled and there were times when a notice had to be displayed, that no performance would be given to less than a given number of people.

At the commencement of the war, the Lanchester Marionette Theatre offered itself as a complete travelling show ready for the road to E.N.S.A. but this was politely refused. For the first year of the war the Theatre toured the country, playing to evacuated and non-evacuated children, and many other shows to the public in general. After repeated efforts to join E.N.S.A., they were accepted and started touring for that organisation towards the end of 1941. For over a year they travelled up and down England playing to the troops in all sorts of places and conditions, from a mere handful in a village school hall or camp hut, to the larger hall of the "garrison theatre". There were many adventures, on tour, in all sorts of weather, fog, snow, mud, but there were many pleasant trips during the summer. The programme presented to the troops was the same as that given elsewhere and included the famous "Underwater Ballet" and "Circus". The troops were some of the best and most appreciative audiences the Marionettes have played to. The E.N.S.A. tour finished early in 1943.

After this the Marionettes underwent a renovation but they were soon on the road again to fulfil engagements that had been accumulating from schools and colleges together with shows for "War Weapons Week", "Holidays at Home" and similar events. During this period the Marionettes had performed in places where The Council for the Encouragement of Music and Art (now the Arts Council of Great Britain) regularly sent their concerts. These tours took the Marionettes all over the country, and at times C.E.M.A. "loaned" them to the British Council, who arranged a visit to American Hospitals where Waldo Lanchester and his wife "roughed it", sleeping in huts and living with the American staff on the wind-swept Wiltshire Downs. On another occasion they were "loaned" to the Y.M.C.A., who arranged for them to visit Naval bases on the West coast of Scotland, and Northern Ireland.

Between these engagements, they gave short seasons at their own little Theatre in Malvern, but this eventually proved too small and closed down early in 1946.

A milestone was reached in December, 1945, when they spent a week at the Theatre Royal, Bristol. The theatre holds 600, it is one of the oldest in the country, the visit proving to be very successful. From then the Marionettes went from strength to strength. They had a three weeks season at the Birmingham Repertory Theatre, in 1947, going from there to the first Edinburgh Festival and giving morning performances in a super cinema holding 2,000, to their largest ever audience, 1,700. Another important event was the production, at the desire and with the helps of the Arts Council, of the early Madrigal Opera *L'Amfiparnaso,* by Orazio Vecchi (1597); the Lanchesters made the marionettes, and the madrigals were sung by the New English Singers, directed by Cuthbert Kelly. A London première was given at the Wigmore Hall, December, 1946, with a repeat performance again with the Singers a month later. The New English Singers made a set of records of the Opera frequently used when the Marionettes visit Music Societies.

In June of 1949 *The Birmingham Post,* in association with Sir Barry Jackson and the Arts Council, staged the British Theatre Exhibition in Birmingham and a Marionette Theatre was built for the Lanchesters, where they performed four times a day to packed houses. On the outer walls of the

Theatre were displayed their collection of old English Marionettes and Posters with other loaned exhibits.

Then came the exciting news that Bernard Shaw had consented to write the Marionettes a short playlet, featuring himself as Shakespeare, entitled *Shakes v. Shaw*. This was recorded by a famous cast, headed by Sir Lewis Casson as Shakespeare and Ernest Thesiger as Shaw, and was first performed at the 1949 Malvern Festival. Some day this little play will be a valuable document in dramatic history.

Festival of Britain year, 1951, saw the Marionettes at the Riverside Theatre, in the Festival Pleasure Gardens, Battersea Park, a return visit to the Bath Assembly, Stratford-upon-Avon, and Nottingham. Performances of *L'Amfiparnaso* with the New English Singers were given again at Wigmore Hall, and at the Hovingham Music Festival.

The company participates in all functions of national interest such as recent attendances at the 1962 Punch Celebrations at Covent Garden and the First International Puppet Festival at Colwyn Bay in May, 1963.

III.—Scotland's Wooden Company have their Theatre at 4 Belgrave Mews, Edinburgh. Behind the swing doors stood the auditorium and proscenium of the smallest theatre in Scotland. Decor both inside and out is simple, but effective—such as flowers growing from gaily-painted beer barrels. Puppet-master is Miles Lee, a quiet-spoken Yorkshireman who has again established a home for puppetry in Scotland. He began to search for suitable premises as far back as 1946. It was 1950 before he found them, and he and his partner, Olivia Hopkins, a former teacher of art, began in earnest to build up their public.

They decorated the theatre themselves, made their own puppets—each at a cost of between 30/- and £3, and ten days' hard work. They wrote their own plays: *The Hare and the Fox, A Tale of Tails, The Shepherdess and the Sweep.*

In between regular seasons in Edinburgh they loaded their scenery, curtain and lighting equipment into a Bedford truck and toured the islands of the north and west, bumping over chaotic roads to play in tiny halls packed with crofters.

Once again, too, the Wooden Company is back on the roads of Scotland—for although the Lee Puppet Company is permanently based in Edinburgh, the two partners and their 160 performers have travelled many thousands of miles between Shetland and the Border.

Their programmes constitute a most popular "fringe" activity at The Edinburgh Festival of Music and The Arts in August/September.

IV.—THE ERIC BRAMALL MARIONETTE THEATRE. This company of 400 puppets, expressive witnesses of Eric Bramall's experience as a puppet showman, are his own creation, designed, devised and dressed as his widening experience advised. In twelve years he has presented all kinds of puppets, glove, string, rod and shadow puppets, in theatre, music hall, ballroom, television studio, and department store. He has appeared in pantomime, revue, variety bill and cabaret. Under the auspices of the Arts Council he has presented his show for Art Societies and Colleges. He has toured and has had resident seasons. He entertains at Children's Parties, at Men Only Dinners, Women's Clubs, Old Folk's Gatherings and Youth Clubs. Obviously Mr. Bramall does not cater for a specialised audience. But this is not intended as an advertisement for Mr. Bramall but to suggest rather that puppets have not merely a narrow and limited appeal.

To have been so fully occupied as a popular entertainer has no doubt brought handsome rewards, and yet in October, 1957, Mr. Bramall laid aside the puppets which had brought him some measure of renown, and launched a programme of pure puppetry which he called *The New Puppetry*. This was most unusual fare, many of his puppets were simple objects such as table tennis balls, and rolls of parchment paper, others were Surrealistic, some bizarre, none were conventional, but the programme emphasised the puppetesque qualities of puppets.

Unfortunately British newspapers show little interest in puppetry as an art, and since there are so few writers qualified to criticise a programme of puppetry, *The New Puppetry* did not arouse the attention it possibly deserved. This revolutionary puppetry will gain a wider viewing in the near future, but not during the first season at the Harlequin. For this reason *The New Puppetry* is not dealt with fully here, but in all the Bramall acts, that is, in his popular and New Puppetry programmes, puppets are nothing but puppets, they are not substitutes for actors. Much of their attraction and entertainment value is in their ability to do so many things that a human actor—or any human being—cannot do. His puppets, as all good puppets under good guidance, have a telling power of suggestion, they will satirize, burlesque and exaggerate human movement, they will highlight human idiosyncrasies but they will always behave in a manner peculiar to his puppets and display characteristics of their purposeful design. No matter how they move, how expertly they are manipulated, they call for the imagination of the audience, even when he indulges in giving his puppets realistic movements. For instance, in a recent television series Mr. Bramall showed a diminutive puppet clambering up to the platform. The studio audience applauded the well-timed movements. The puppet still clambered unsuccessfully in his effort to reach the top. The little puppet hands firmly gripped the edge of the platform, and the legs moved so that knees or feet could gain a foothold. It seemed the marionette would burst a blood vessel, or his skin, or his trousers. The programme ended with the puppet still vainly clambering. During the following week viewers wrote letters pleading that the puppet should be allowed to reach safety.

In the mind's eye of viewers the platform had become a precipice, and every calculated and deftly manipulated movement of the puppet made to convey an impression of frustration and desperate struggle, produced an atmosphere of suspense and tension seldom created by means of puppetry.

Eric Bramall obviously relishes adding macabre touches and giving a Grand Guignol treatment to many of his acts. In the New Puppetry programme he has more deaths than there are in an Elizabethan tragedy, but this flair does not smother the delicacy with which he stages an idyll or gay fantasy. This happy disposition to use diverse means of communicating points of view has suggested to one writer an idea for a puppet play, in which Eric Bramall will be seen linking arms with children, skeletons, fairy tale princesses, ghouls, Japanese heroines, vampires, lambs and lions.

He has added to his achievements the founding of the International Festival held for the first time at Colwyn Bay in May, 1963, and described on a subsequent page.

THE HOGARTH PUPPETS

This troupe was founded before the war by Jan Bussell, who now enjoys a world-wide reputation. His following in Britain was greatly increased when he became a producer for the B.B.C., first on sound radio (Children's Hour), where, together with his wife Ann Hogarth, and the late Annette Mills, his team made *Muffin the Mule* into a sort of national puppet-emblem that later became a very popular toy. The troupe is equally familiar to B.B.C. television viewers. It is currently based on Egham, Surrey ("Karlmede", 16 Riverside), from which Jan Bussell operates his CARAVAN THEATRE and travels widely.

During the summer months he gives performances under London County Council auspices at London's Park and Open Spaces—introducing many children of the built-up areas to the fun and experience of live puppet theatre.

L.C.C. Parks Entertainment Programmes may be purchased direct from County Hall, London, S.E.1.

Other puppeteers with highly individual approaches are: —

Barry Smith, c/o Royal Academy of Dramatic Art, Gower Street, W.C.1, who presents a sophisticated repertoire of glove-puppet shows, mainly for adults and the young in heart.

Jane Phillips, 22 Church Road, Christchurch, Glamorganshire, plays to Welsh children, using music and Welsh tradition.

SHADOW PUPPETS

Lotte Reiniger, Abbey Art Centre, 89 Park Road, Barnet, Herts. (Barnet 7982.)

Olive Blackham, c/o British Puppet and Model Theatre Guild.

Helen Binyon, c/o Bath Academy of Art, Bath, Somerset.

OTHER PUPPET TROUPES

Ark Puppet Theatre, 89 Mount Ararat Road, Richmond, Surrey. Tel.: Richmond 3840. (Marionettes.)

Arno Puppets (Mable and Carol Crowther), 250 West Barnes Lane, Malden, Surrey. Tel.: MALden 1068. (Marionettes, Glove Puppets, Magic, Punch & Judy.)

The Berrymor Puppets (Doris Mortimer), 46 Northumberland Avenue, Wanstead Park, London, E.12. Tel.: Wanstead 2893. (Glove Puppets.)

Bidston's Puppets, 46 Ferndale Road, Hoylake, Wirral, Cheshire. (Dramatic Hand-puppets.)

Roy Blatchford, 59 Lyddesdale Avenue, Anchorsholme, Blackpool, Lancs. (Marionettes.)

Eric Bramall, F.R.S.A., H.R.C.A., The Mews House, Penrhyn Bay, Llandudno, Caernarvonshire. Tel.: Penrhynside 39578. (Glove Puppets, Exciting Puppetry of all kinds.)

Combe Martin Puppet Society, Libra Gardens, Combe Martin, Devon. Tel.: Combe Martin 3364. (String Marionettes.)

John Dudley, Stort House, Sawbridgeworth, Herts. Tel.: Sawbridgeworth 2302. (Dudley TV Marionettes, Glove Puppets, Punch & Judy, Cabaret Puppets Magic, M.C., Toastmaster.)

Fisher's Puppet Theatre (directed by Herbert Fisher), 117 St. James' Drive, London, S.W.17. Tel.: BALham 5753. (Marionette Shows, Variety, Cabaret, Clubs, Parties, Schools, Advertising.)

"Giles" Puppets, 37 Gipsy Lane, Wokingham. Tel.: Wokingham 341. (Puppets in UV lighting for all occasions.)

Gulliver's Puppets (George Wall-Man), 60 Bickersteth Road, London, S.W.17. Tel.: BALham 9767. (Marionettes, Royal Punch & Judy, Magic, Ventriloquism.)

The Israel Marionettes, c/o Harold Aidalberry, 46 Northumberland Avenue, Wanstead Park, E.12. Tel.: Wanstead 2893. (Marionettes.)

The Jacquard Puppets (directed by John Carr, O.B.E.), 57 Ridgeview Road, Whetstone, N.20. Tel.: Hillside 1356. (Marionettes.)

Tom Kemp, 22 Willoughby Road, London, N.W.3. Tel.: HAMpstead 2688. (Punch & Judy, Magic, Ventriloquism. Nursery Puppets.)

Sam Kemp and Margaret Cook (The Playhouse Puppets), 96 Streathbourne Road, Tooting Bec Common, S.W.17. Tel.: BALham 5140. (String Marionettes.)

The Laurey Puppets, The Studio, Tiptree, Essex. Tel.: Tiptree 333. (Glove and String Puppets.)

Les Theatres des Petites Poupees (The Theatre of the Little Dolls) (Phyllis and Reginald S. Miles), Orchard Cottage, Dower Avenue, Wallington, Surrey. (Marionettes.)

Les Nottle, 74 Cherrydown Avenue, Chingford, London, E.4. Tel.: SILverthorn 5591. (Punch & Judy, Clowning, Magic.)

Lilliput Marionette Theatre, 31 Avondale Road, Wolverhampton, and 5 The Bishop's Avenue, London, N.2. Tel.: TUDor 7840. (Marionette Plays.)

Little World Theatre (The Da Silvas), 19 Hill Street, Wisbech, Cambs. Tel.: Wisbech 1243. (Marionettes, Punch, Rod and Glove Puppets.)

Marlborough Marionettes (Mr. and Mrs. R. Davis), 47 Watford Road, St. Albans, Herts. (Marionettes.)

Mejandes Marionettes (L. Murial Shutt), 7 Lupus Street, London, S.W.1. Tel.: TATe Gallery 4871. (Marionettes, Puppets made to order.)

Merryman Marionettes (The), 27 Colgrove Road, Loughborough, Leics. Tel.: Loughborough 2451. (Marionettes.)

Middleton Marionettes, 1 Middleton Way, Carshalton, Surrey. Tel.: CROydon 2181 (business hours only). (Marionettes, Variety.)

Northern Children's Marionette Theatre, 26 Chapel Street, Leeds Road, Bradford, Yorks. Tel.: 31290. (Entertainment for children.)

Paul and Peta Page, The Old Bakery, Takeley Street, nr. Bishops Stortford, Herts. (Puppets.)

Playhouse Puppets (The) (S. P. Kemp), Puppetcraft Workshop at 96 Streathbourne Road, Tooting Bec, S.W.17. Tel.: BALham 5140. (Marionettes.)

Pompet Puppets, 31 Barnfield Road, Belvedere, Kent. Tel.: Erith (ET) 36313. (Glove Puppet, Punch & Judy.)

The Dave Poppy Puppets, "Sunstar", Pensarn Farm, Alteryn, Newport, Mon. (Marionettes, Cabaret.)

Ristland Glove Puppets, 31 Leeward Road, West Worthing, Sussex. Tel.: Worthing 1051. (Jimmy Ginger's Favourite Fairy Tales.)

The Simms Marionettes, 71 Vivian Road, Sketty, Swansea. Tel.: 22652. (Marionettes.)

Ray Smith, 31 Avondale Road, Wolverhampton. (Freeland Puppeteer, 1962 summer season with Dudley Marionettes, winter season with The Lilliput Marionette Coy.)

The Stavordale Marionettes, 122 Regents Park Road, Finchley, London, N.3. Tel.: FINchley 4066. (Marionettes and Glove Puppets.)

Fred Tickner, 31 Ridgeway Avenue, Gravesend, Kent. (Punch
& Judy Marionettes.)

"Uncle Jim" (J. D. Osborn, M.I.M.), 41 Sidegate Lane, Ips-
wich, Suffolk. (Punch & Judy Marionettes.)

"Uncle Smoky" (Ronnie Townsend, V.A.F.), 39 Tweeddale
Green, Carshalton, Surrey. Tel.: FAIrlands 7959.
(Musical Clown, Punch & Judy, Magic.)

Violet and Pantopuck, 13 Dartmouth Park Road, London,
N.W.5. Tel.: GULliver 3840. (Glove Puppets.)

The Walford Puppets (Mr. and Mrs. K. N. Crawford), 17
Long Hyde, Shephall, Stevenage, Herts. (Marionettes and
Rod Puppets.)

The Worth Puppets, 11 Hemyock Road, Birmingham 29.
Tel.: Priory 2516. (Glove Puppets.)

*   *   *

FOR CHILDREN'S PARTIES AND
SPECIAL ENTERTAINMENT

The Children's Party Agency, 32 Edge Street, W.8 (PARk
8476), provides puppet shows and a particularly brilliant one
about a Frog; Punch & Judy Shows, and equally original
diversions. Literature on enquiry.

*   *   *

PROFESSIONAL PUNCH AND JUDY
"PROFESSORS"

Punch and Judy "Professors" operate in various parts of
the country, some all the year round, others at seasonal
pitches in seaside resorts, etc. The majority belong to the
BPMTG. They responded *en masse* by attending the Mister
Punch Tercentenary Celebrations (summer, 1962) at St. Paul's
Church, Covent Garden. (Fully reported to *The Puppet
Master*, Vol. 7, No. 1.)

The Professors are normally available for bookings at
children's parties and will travel far outside their home-based
addresses. The latter are listed below: —

"Keno", 10 Dowshes Gardens, Kelvedon, Colchester, Essex.
(T) Kelvedon 349. (Brochure.)

Professor John Stafford, 37a Fernicombe Road, Roxall, Paignton, Devon. (T) Paignton 57049. (Brochure.)

Hugh Cecil, 82 Kings Avenue, New Malden, Surrey. (T) Malden 3917. (Brochure.)

Joe Barnes (Uncle Joe), 52 Sherbourne Gardens, Prittlewell, Southend-on-Sea, Essex. (T) Southend 47312. (Brochure.)

Gus Woods, 14 Narford Road, Clapton, E.5. (T) UPP 7192. (Brochure.)

Frank Norman, 18 Carshalton Place, Carshalton, Surrey. (T) Wallington 2675.

J. W. Martindale, 37 Thirlmere Street, West Hartlepool.

F. W. Miller ("Dustini"), Holly Bank, Rue Wood, nr. Wem, Salop.

W. Llewellyn, 13 Barrington Road, Newton Aycliff, Co. Durham.

Peter Goodhall, 174 Ferryraft Road, Yadebridge, Hemel Hempstead, Herts.

John Redber, The Wessex Puppet Theatre, 29 West Allington, Bridport, Dorset.

Percy Best, 59 Marston Street, Cowley Road, Oxford. (Brochure.)

Steve Gawley, "Uncle" Steve, 176 Bexhill Road, Brighton 7, Sussex.

Stanley Marelle, 27 Woodthorpe Road, Kings Heath, Birmingham 14. (Brochure.)

Charles Tomkins, 130 Richmond Park Road, Kingston, Surrey.

Arthur Hambling, 13 Wellhouse Road, Maidenhead, Berks.

Les Nottle, 74 Cherrydown Avenue, Chingford, Essex. (T) Silverthorne 5591. (Brochure.)

Tom Kemp, 22 Willoughby Road, Hampstead, N.W.3. (T) HAM 2688. (Brochure.)

Tony Green, "Delma", Hazlemere, High Wycombe, Bucks. (T) Holmer Green 2141.

Percy Press ("Uncle Percy"), 43 Fitzroy Road, Regents Park, N.W.1. (T) PRImrose 2723. (Brochure.)

Leslie Press ("Uncle" Leslie), 29 Western Road, Wood Green, N.22. (T) BOWes Park 4405. (Brochure.)

Professor R. Codman, 44 Farnworth Street, Kensington, Liverpool 6. (T) ANField 5617. (Brochure.)

Professor H. S. Codman, 8a Mostyn Street, Llandudno, N. Wales.

R. Townsend, "Smoky, the Clown", 39 Tweeddale Green, Carshalton, Surrey. (T) FAIrlands 7959. (Brochure.)

Professor F. Edmonds, 56 Western Avenue, Blacon, Chester. (T) Chester 24543. Summer residence: The Beach, Weymouth, Dorset.

Professor A. Smith, Summer residence: The Beach, Margate, Kent.

George Wallman, 60 Bickersteth Road, London, S.W.17. (T) BALham 9767. (Brochure.)

Francis Keep ("Uncle" Boko), 15 Uxbridge Road, London, W.7. EALing 2660. (Brochure.)

Charles Magill, "The Owls", 36 Mt. Ephraim Lane, Streatham, S.W.16. (T) STR 2118. (Brochure.)

George Rissen, 85 Somerville Road, Chadwell Heath, Romford, Essex. (T) Seven Kings 4198. (Brochure.)

SOME TELEVISION PUPPETEERS

Harry Corbett, creator of *Sooty*. (B.B.C.)

Jan and Vlasta Dalibor, creators of *Pinky & Perky*. (I.T.V.)

Janet Nickolls, creator of *Pussy Cat Willum*. (I.T.V.)

Gordon Murray, producer at the B.B.C. Puppet Theatre.

Audrey Atterbury, creator of *Andy Pandy*, and *Woodentops*. (B.B.C.)

* * *

SOME FILM PUPPETEERS

John Blundell, Christine Fletcher, and Judith Shutt, creators of *Four Feather Falls* and *Supercar*. (A.P. Films Ltd.)

Roberta Leigh, creator of *Torchy*, *Hoppity* and

Peter Elliott Hayes, creator of *Noddy* and *Here Comes Kandy*.

* * *

PUPPET MAKERS

An established craftswoman specialist is Anna Marita, who also animates and dresses Wooden Dutch Dolls. She may be contacted c/o Heals Ltd., the furnishing store in Tottenham Court Road, W.C.1. Miss Marita has been associated as a demonstrator and operator with the famous manufacturers of Pelham Puppets. Private address: 1a Duke Street, Manchester Square, W.1. WEL. 0049. Pelham Puppets have a Children's Club with its own Magazine.

* * *

The following makers will design and manufacture special orders to customers' own requirements, for display and exhibition purposes; for puppet troupes and theatres; television, or more eclectic media: —

John Carr, 57 Ridgeway Road, Whetstone, London, N.20. (HIL. 1356.)

Jack Whitehead, "The Keel", Fishbourne, Isle of Wight.

Fred Rickner, "Morven", 31 Ridgeway Avenue, Gravesend, Kent.

Mr. and Mrs. Ernest Shutt, 7 Lupus Street, S.W.1. (TAT 4871.)

Desmond McNamara, 1 Woodchurch Road, N.W.3. (MAI. 1224.) Specialises in pâpier maché objects for children's pantomimes; display and exhibition work, surrealistic, grotesque and traditional; elaborate articulated puppets—people, animals and impossible creatures; modelling of all kinds. Is an authority on *The New Art of Papier Mâché*, published by McGibbon & Kee.

* * *

Gerald Morice has earned a worldwide reputation in the field of puppetry, having been active in the Union Internationale des Marionettes. He lives at Edith Lodge, Graham Road, Malvern, and was co-founder of the B.P.M.T.G. 35 years ago. Writer and researcher on puppet affairs, he reports the day to day scene in a column of *The Stage* (as Charles Trentham), and for many years previously contributed

Punch & Puppet Pars to the *World's Fair,* another weekly, in which his erudition and familiarity with this subject were regularly looked forward to by readers. His vast private collection of documents, puppetry objects, and library is of much interest to historians.

*   *   *

GREETING CARDS
Puppet Dolls photographed in colour from originals made by *Helena* are reproduced as greeting cards published in the Azalia Series, at 35 Wellington Square, London, S.W.3.

RARE BOOKS
Collectors' items, second-hand an out-of-print editions of books on Puppetry are sought, and often found at K. R. Drummond, Bookseller, 21 Little Russell Street, Bloomsbury, W.C.1. (CHA. 2300.)

PHOTOGRAPHIC ARCHIVE
An impressive file of photographs (black-and-white) and colour slides is available from Tom Howard, 5 Greystoke Gardens, Enfield West, Middlesex.

FURTHER READING
"Puppetry Fundamentals", by A. R. Philpotts (Pantopuck), available from the Sales Secretary, E.P.A., 23a Southampton Place, London, W.C.1. Price 2/6, post free. This little gem of a book sets out the basic facts about puppet theatre, how it differs from human theatre, and what the essential requirements for successful puppetry are. It points out the fundamental principles which govern choice of puppet, stage, lighting, scenery, production, speech, etc., with a short chapter on each. So many books on puppets, written by people who have only a limited knowledge of puppet making and little, if any, of performing, advocate dogmatic ways of dealing with puppets which completely rule out further experiment and purpose. This book will ensure that beginners in future may start with the right approach to the puppet theatre.

George Speaight is the acknowledged British historian of puppetry, and his book *History of the English Puppet Theatre* (Harrap) is a standard reference on all aspects. It traces in detail the development of the early showmen, the popular theatre of mimes and masks, from its origins in ancient Greece to its flowering Renaissance Europe. It tells of the Elizabethan motions; of the Restoration Punchinellos; the fashionable marionette theatres of XVIII century London; the sagas of travelling showmen and the remarkable revival of puppetry in our own day as a television medium, and as stimulus in education.

The author's long experience as a puppet showman, and a lifetime's research devoted to his subject bring to the layman a lively picture of theatrical life in days gone by, viewed from an unusual vantage-point The study is thoroughly documented, with extensive notes, a bibliography and two appendices giving lists of all English puppet showmen for the period 1600 to 1914.

Owner of a remarkable private collection covering Puppetry, the Juvenile Drama, and Punch and Judy material, George Speaight was originator of the *Old Time Marionettes,* and early Victorian troupe revived at the Festival Gardens, during the Festival of Britain Year, 1961.

PUPPET THEATRE
Production and Manipulation
by MILES LEE

For some time the amateur pupeteer has felt the need for guidance on what to do with his puppets, once he has made them. So little has been written on how, why or what the puppet may perform that the amateur has had to content himself largely with the craft side of making puppets. Now Miles Lee's book fills this need. All aspects of the producer's work receive attention: the theory of puppetry; the artistic and educational uses of puppets; the producer's preparatory

140

work on a play; the planning of movement and grouping; the uses and plotting of lighting; puppet speech, acting and voice differentiation; and the making and selection of puppet plays. A section of the book is devoted to manipulation methods and exercises, and these should prove of the greatest value to educational workers as well as to amateur puppeteers.

Miles Lee's puppet theatre is widely known for its tours in Scotland, northern England, Scandinavia and Iceland, as well as for its regular season in the Mews Theatre during the Edinburgh Festival. With a frontispiece and more than 50 line drawings. 21s. net.

PUPPETS AND PLAYS

by MARJORIE BATCHELDER and VIRGINIA COMER

This is an American puppet book, which has a refreshingly different approach to the subject. Although essentially an educational book dealing with puppetry for schools, it concentrates on the actual use of puppets rather than on the details of construction and jointings, on which much has already been written. It really tells one what to do with puppets and how they can be used creatively. In the best educational sense, by various groups—in fact this picture of what is being done in the United States is a challenge to our own educationalists.

The illustrations are excellent, and many teachers should find inspiration from them as well as in the discussion of the various "projects" and the description of very rapid methods of making puppets from cardboard boxes, tin cans and paper. With 35 illustrations from photographs and 20 line drawings. 21s. net.

* * *

Batchelder, M., *The Puppet Theatre Handbook*. (Jenkins.) H.P. & M.

Beaumont, C., *Puppets and Puppetry*. (Studio.) 1958. H.P. & M.

Blackham, O., *Shadow Puppets*. (Barrie and Rockliff.) 1960.

Bramall, E., *Puppet Plays and Playwriting*. (Bell.) 1961.

Bramall, E., *Making a Start with Marionettes*. (Bell.) 1960.

Bussell, J., *The Puppet Theatre*. F. & F.

Fisher, D., *Wooden Stars*. Boardman.

Lanchester, W. S., *Hand Puppets and String Puppets*. (Dryad Press.) 9th Revised Edition. 1957.

Lee, M., *Puppet Theatre*. (Faber.) 1958. H.P. & M.

Marsh, W. A., *Plays and Patterns for Glove Puppets*. (Harrap.) 1955.

McCrea, L., *Puppets and Puppet Plays*. (O.U.P.) 1949.

McMahon, J., Making and Playing Marionettes. (Harrap.) 1957.

Merten, G., *The Marionette*. Nelson. 1957.

Mulholland, J., *Practical Puppetry* (Jenkins.) Autumn 1961.

Murray, G., *Puppets*. (Puffin Book.)

Obratztsov, S., *The Chinese Puppet Theatre*. (Faber.) 1961.

Speaight, G., *The History of the English Puppet Theatre*. (Harrap.) 1955.

Wall, L. V., and White, G. A., *The Complete Puppet Book*. (Faber.) Revised Edition. 1956.

Whanslaw, H. W., *Animal Puppetry*. (Wells Gardner Darton.) 1948.

    Everybody's Marionette Book. (Wells Gardner Darton.) New Edition reprint. 1957.

    The Bankside Book of Puppets. (Wells Gardner Darton.)

    A Bench Book of Puppetry. (Wells Gardner Darton.) 1957.

    Shadow Play. (Wells Gardner Darton.) 1950.

    The Bankside Stage Book. (Wells Gardner Darton.)

    Bible Puppetry. (Religious Education Press.) 1st Edition reprint. 1958.

    and Hotchkiss, V., *Specialised Puppetry*. (Wells Gardner Darton.) 1948.

Wright, J., *Your Puppetry*. (Sylvan Press.) 1951.

MUSEUM COLLECTIONS

Falling between its function as an ethnographic or theatrical object illustrating social history, and its undeniable role as a child's plaything, the marionette and/or Punch and Judy entourage, do not receive in the United Kingdom the same attention from museums as in some other countries, where permanent exhibitions provide unusual insight into fashions in popular entertainment and episodes of theatrical history.

House-room for puppets is still the exception, not the rule, and in order to discover sometimes whether puppets may be lying out of sight and unclassified patience and persistence may be necessary.

The increased stimulus afforded by puppeteers, as well as enthusiasts in the Society, for Theatre History, or the Toy Museum, should lead to more attention being devoted to this field by professional museum people.

The Victoria and Albert Museum exhibits some examples. The Horniman Museum has a fair variety, including those made by Eastern and primitive people. The Toy Museum at Rottingdean has on view children's string, and glove puppets from several lands, and a toy Punch and Judy set. The Edinburgh Museum of Childhood is in the process of building up its excellent nucleus.

At the British Museum one may see a fine set of rod-puppets from Burma made of skin. Still used traditionally in folk-plays in the Far East, this type is flat in shape. In the old days it used to be just a cut-out in leather. You did not look at the puppet; it was behind a screen, and what you looked at was the shadow, so there was no need for the puppet to be anything but a piece of cardboard.

In some parts of the Far East women were not allowed to sit in the audience of shadow plays, but they were allowed to see the puppets being worked behind the screen, and so some of the figures were elaborated for their benefit. They were made of wax, built up layer by layer, which gave the colour a translucent quality.

INTERNATIONAL PUPPET FESTIVAL

Britain's first International Puppet Festival held at Colwyn Bay, Denbighshire, from May 20th to 25th, 1963. This year puppets and their admirers came from many different countries.

Mr. Eric Bramall was Festival Director and the importance of the event is indicated by the fact that it was sponsored by the Borough Council and supported by the Arts Council of Great Britain. Besides the Harlequin Theatre iself, several other theatres were used for performances during the Festival week—the Rhos Playhouse, the Prince of Wales Theatre and the Colwyn Bay Pier Pavilion.

Some of the world's leading companies participated in the Festival. From Germany, for example came Harro Siegel of Brunswick the Stuttgart Rod-Puppet Theatre and the Deutsches Institut fur Puppetspiel (Bochum); from Poland, the "Arlekin" State Puppet Theatre of Lodz; from Switzerland, the Fred Schnekenburger Company; and two companies from the United States, George Latshaw's Puppets and Lloyds' "International". Several other countries also represented, including France, India, Japan and Russia, indicate that this inaugural event may become a regular occasion.

The strong contingent of British companies, headed by the Harlequin Theatre's own permanent residents under the direction of Eric Bramall, included Jan Bussell and Ann Hogarth with the latest production of the Hogarth Puppets; the Stavordale Marionettes in their unique puppet cabaret; performances by Jane Phillip's Caricature Theatre, the Company of Five; and the Lanchester Marionettes, one of the oldest and most revered of British puppet companies. Britain's most traditional puppet, the incorrigible rogue "Mr. Punch" will be presented by Percy Press, our leading Punch and Judy performer.

A Festival Club, where puppeteers and enthusiasts gathered after the performances; an exhibition of "Masterpieces of the Puppet-maker's Art" showed a unique collection of puppets of all types from different parts of the world; and the Denbigh-shire Art Society's display of "Puppet-inspired Art" presented paintings, pottery, and book-jacket designs. Other attractions were films, an exhibition of dolls of the world lent by the Lakeland Doll Society, and an exhibition of Victorian toy theatres and modern model theatres. Local bookshops also joined in the occasion by stressing the puppet theme; and, of course, there were plenty of opportunities for visitors to tour the Snowdonian mountains, the grand coastal scenery, the historic castles of North Wales and the peaceful Isle of Anglesey—all looking at their best in the blossoming month of May.

TOY THEATRES

The Toy Theatre in England originated in the early days of the Regency as a kind of theatrical souvenir. Portraits of famous actors and actresses of the time were sold for a penny, plain; or twopence, coloured.

These forerunners of the pin-ups of today were often embellished by tinsel, velvet, or silk applications.

In late-Victorian, or Edwardian England, when live Theatre and Music Hall played a vital part in the national life, boys and girls were given "the penny plain, twopence coloured" toy and thus developed during the formative years a love for, and understanding of, stage productions. It is remarkable to discover the number of men ranking among the world's great, who pay tribute to the fun and games they enjoyed during their childhood with what has come to be called "Juvenile Drama".

Although very popular in England, and now sought avidly by American collectors interested in the quaint and the antique, Toy Theatres never caught on so much in the United States as did, for example, Magic Lanterns.

J. K. Green claims to have been "the original inventor" and publisher of Juvenile Theatrical Prints. In 1808 he seems to have been the first to publish all the characters in a play, together with sheets of scenery and a simplified book of words. His engraved copper-plates were subsequently acquired by one of his most go-ahead agents, John Redington, whose "wholesale and retail Theatrical print and tinsel warehouse" was situated in Hoxton Street, London, long since demolished.

In 1876, Redington died and his shop and stock of copper-plates were left to his son-in-law, Benjamin Pollock, who devoted his life to making Toy Theatres and to reprinting the plays which Redington and Green had previously published. Benjamin Pollock's name became widely associated with the craft that the products became known as "Pollock Toy Theatres". On his death in 1937, the shop was carried on by Miss Pollock until it was destroyed during the bombing of London.

The tradition, however, has been kept alive. Exact replicas of the Pollock Toy Theatres are manufactured today at 44 Monmouth Street, Cambridge Circus, W.C.2, from which a thriving business has been built up catering for a growing demand for *theatre* as against *telly,* which seemed an inevitable reaction. Discerning parents who nostalgically remember the role played ancestrally by Toy Theatres in their family circle, now look to the Pollock shop for inspiration.

A gaily-coloured catalogue designed by P. Adams Turner has for its cover a reproduction of a Pollock Stage. Its contents include an excerpt from Robert Louis Stevenson's famous essay of 1887, paying homage to that exciting play-pattern to be later known as "Skeltery", after Skelt—another publisher. Other information for the enthusiast describes the different styles of theatre fronts, e.g., "The Regency"; "The Adelphi" and "The Victoria". There are pictures of characters from the plays: lists of the plays themselves; scenic accessories like wire slides, lighting sets, orchestra strips, and copies of the original sheets.

The stock of old "penny plain" sheets is not quite exhausted. As far as possible these sheets are collated into complete sets, but in some cases it will be necessary to substitute similar scenes from other plays. It is hoped gradually to fill in the gaps by new engravings taken from the original copper and zinc plates. Unfortunately this cannot always be done, as some of the plates no longer exist or are too worn and damaged to be used, in which case photostat copies can be made by special arrangement.

Sheets of scenes and characters from the following plays are available. Price, 6d. each plain; or 1/6 each, coloured, according to the traditional recipes.

Play	Publisher	No. of Sheets in Play
Baron Munchausen	Redington	26
Battle of Waterloo	Green, 1842	26
The Blind Boy	Park	17
Blue Jackets	Green, 1842	9
The Brigand	Green, 1836	18
The Corsican Brothers	Green, 1854	13
Charles II	Redington	9
Daughter of the Regiment	Green, 1857	7
Douglas	Green, 1834	11
Don Quixote	Redington	12
Forty Thieves	Green, 1830	33
Jack the Giant Killer	Green, 1854	29
King Henry, or The Miller of Mansfield	Redington	10
Lord Darnley	Green, 1839	14
Lord Mayor's Fool	Green, 1837	8
The Maid and the Magpie	Green, 1841	14
The Miller and his Men	Lloyd	21
The Mistletoe Bough	Redington	14
Oliver Twist	Redington	23
Paul Clifford	Redington	27
Sleeping Beauty	Green, 1851	27
Silver Palace	Green, 1841	12

Timour the Tartar	Green, 1849	19
The Waterman	Green, 1857	7
Woodman's Hut		17

In addition to those above listed, Epinal Prints are offered, hand-coloured, printed in France, c. 1880. In fact, everything to do with the ancient practice of toy theatre may be discovered at the Pollock Shop.

In addition to Toy Theatres, the shop sells Wooden Dutch Dolls dressed by hand in traditional costumes, and offers free admission to a remarkable collection of period toys and dolls on loan from many private sources.

Special Exhibitions of kindred subjects, e.g., Tinsel Pictures, are held occasionally throughout the year.

Collections of the Juvenile Drama

Most private collectors of this *genre* will have had some commerce with The Pollock Shop just mentioned and through its proprietress, Mrs. Fawdry, may be put into contact with fellow collectors.

There are many such throughout Britain, ranging from those who are jealous of their anonymity to those who enjoy sharing information and viewing. Among the latter are many men now eminent in the theatrical profession, who have been named by the late A. E. Wilson, in his books on the subject.

The trend has its equivalent appeal for actors in both Hollywood and Broadway, many of whom have acquired their best things in this country. To name only one, Alfred Lunt, placed his collection on exhibition at the City of Museum, New York, where it creates widespread interest.

The Barnett Collection, containing many fine examples in mint condition, is now incorporated into the Victoria and Albert Museum's Library and archive. Mr. Roland Knaster, whose variegated treasures are mentioned on another page, is the possessor of some rare specimens of Skeltry—theatres, sheets and tinsel pictures.

Another collector, Mr. Ian Sargint, 102 Warwick Gardens, London (whose interests range from old china to Siamese

Cats) began acquiring Tinsel Prints in 1922, and he will correspond with other collectors. He has some uncommon Pollock title-pages, and several original Pollock Theatres which compete for house-room with Dutch silver miniature toys, ikons, and ancient Greek terracotta!

Mr. David Robinson, c/o British Film Institute, 81 Dean Street, London, W.1., collects Toy Theatres and all material appertaining to this field. In over 1,000 Penny Plain sheets he has specimens of every English publisher's output.

That the public interest in Juvenile interest is not merely nostalgic or exclusive, is borne out by the fascination it still holds for the younger generations of art students and those at teacher colleges, and theatrical academies. At Goldsmith's Training College, London, for example, students receive instruction as part of their normal courses in the making, and apppreciation of, Toy Theatres. At this centre they have evolved a peculiar modernistic version and have created exquisite results, using paper sculpture, and evolving an original style based on slightly abstract scenery.

Further information on this subject may be obtained from The British Theatre Museum and Association, 12 Henrietta Street, London, W.C.2. (*Hon. Sec.*: Mrs. Donald Sinden, 60 Temple Fortune Lane, London, N.W.11).

THE MINIATURE THEATRE

Of all exquisite productions where fantasy and craftsmanship are effectively given rein, in a class by itself stands THE MINIATURE THEATRE. There are less than a handful of puppet and marionette people who have dared this complex version of conventional showmanship; and of all these the acknowledged master-craftsman is Clifford Heap.

Operating from his home-base at 219 High Road, Buckhurst Hill, Essex (BUC. 2044), this remarkable artist travels widely and takes his mobile set-up to schools all over the United Kingdom where countless generations of boys and girls have shared in a very stimulating experience.

This is one kind of production which defies descriptive words. You must actually see it to believe that such a miracle of artistry, dramatic feeling, the pleasure of speech, colour, movement music and lighting, exists nowadays. It reproduces, on a minuscule scale, all the thrill of live theatre, the "compactness" of a television screen, and the transportation of imagination induced by Juvenile Drama.

Clifford Heap has spent very many years perfecting his craft. Though he draws on the reservoir of nursery tales and pantomime themes for his productions, these are transformed "into something rich and strange" a blending of dreamworld and reality, which enthrals the younger spectator and captivates grown-up audiences by the sheer beauty of the effect created. The entire programmes are devised and constructed by Clifford Heap, assisted by Douglas Heap who also selects and arrange the music. His wife, Alix Heap, manipulates the superbly designed animated figurines, in the bijoux framework. So that the Heap Miniature Theatre is held together by a family team—and perhaps to this closeness of interest its success may be attributed.

The Tinder Box; Aladdin; Beauty and The Beast—these are only three subjects from the repertoire which draw their inspiration from the drama and simplicity of popular folklore.

They are in demand year after year by Schools and Colleges but during school holidays performances may be arranged as children's treats or at private parties. The troupe has given performances in aid of charity; to help groups with a kindred interest in craftsmanship, like The British Toymakers' Guild; and at some of the intimate Theatre Clubs which arise (and alas pass away so soon) all over London.

Described once as being "the smallest marionettes in the world", even this slogan is inadequate to convey the rapturous faces and expressions of wonderment when the final curtain drops on the enactment of say, *The Sleeping Beauty,* "a fantasy in miniature presented in 14 beautiful scenes with full musical accompaniment".

Through the Miniature Theatre, and its ever-growing popularity, Clifford Heap has given to tens of thousands of people a re-created fairyland and a pristine joy during times when a worried look sits on far too many humans.

*   *   *

CHINESE SHADOWS

"This ingenious instrument consists in moving, by pegs fastened to them, small figures cut out of pasteboard, the joints of which are all pliable, behind a piece of fine painted gauze, placed before an opening in a curtain, in such a manner as to exhibit various scenes, according to pleasure; while the opening covered with gauze is illuminated, towards the apartment where the spectators sit, by means of a light reflected from a mirror, so that the shadows of the pegs are concealed. When it is requisite to cause a figure to perform a variety of movements, it is necessary to have several persons, who must be exceedingly expert. When a snake is to be represented gliding, the figure, which consists of delicate rings, must be directed, at least by three assistants.

"This amusement, which one can hardly see the first time without pleasure, is a Chinese invention. Many years ago, Chinese boxes were seen, on which such moveable figures were apparent only when the box was held against the light. In China, these shadows are used at the well-known feast of lanterns."

From "Recreations in Science; or, A Complete Series of Rational Amusement". London. 1830.

PART V

TOY SOLDIERS AND MODEL SOLDIERS

Long before Hans Andersen immortalized toy soldiers in his fairy story, these little warriors had been the companions of children from the earliest times. Like the doll, the early miniatures also served a religious or commemorative purpose as well as being playthings. Some of these, found in ancient Egyptian tombs, are now in Cairo Museum.

During the last thirty years or so a growing interest has been observed in children's playthings, both for their intrinsic and often artistic value, and also as a delightful aspect of social history. After many years of neglect they are being assiduously collected, and researches are being made into their origins. To those who, in their childhood, played with lead soldiers, or who today purchase them for their children, it may come as a surprise to know that the history of these little figures goes back to the time of the ancient Egyptians, and that throughout the succeeding centuries they have been the most popular of all playthings for boys.

Surviving military figures from Roman and medieval times, are probably talismans or souvenirs, but up to the 18th century, carved wooden soldier-figures were the regular playthings of peasant boys, as were models in silver and gold of princelings.

Until the advent of mass production of the lead, or tin, soldier there was little distinction between model and toy. But after that, a distinction arose—the latter tending to be crude and inaccurate, although preserving that certain charm which belongs to toys proper. This lead soldier originated in Germany in the mid-18th century. Nuremberg had become the great centre for the industry. Many millions of pieces were cast. Although the size varied, all German production was of one particular style—the "flat" figure.

France was the first country to mass-produce the solid, all-round Soldier. This began at the time of the Revolution and the original firm continues to do so to this day.

Then in London, during the 1890's William Britain produced a round "hollow-cast" Soldier to the scale of the then popular No. 1 Railway Gauge. This size has, with very little changes, come down to us today as the "standard size". Britain's idea of the hollow-cast soldier was originally a family secret but eventually it was copied by many other makes as it used less metal, and so was cheaper. Very many types of this sort have been made in Britain and Europe and, together with the German-made flat soldier, have come to predominate in nursery-floor war-games, or "Little Wars", as H. G. Wells called them, in a book by that title which he wrote.

After the Second World War toy soldiers began to be made in plastic materials and at first they were not popular. In the last few years, however, improved techniques, and some beautiful designs, have made them more attractive to children. Adult collectors, however, still have a preference for metal ones.

Toy soldiers have been made in other materials to. For 200 years paper and cardboard cut-out figures have been popular, the centre of their manufacture being Strasbourg, in East France. Also, for several centuries the Gingerbread Men had military cousins, made of gum, coated with sugar and baked in an oven. Peter III of Russia, who was a somewhat eccentric ruler, is said to have been particularly devoted to them, and once had a rat sentenced to death by court martial for eating one!

Collecting toy and model soldiers can be both a source of pleasure and very instructive. Some toy designs are most carefully moulded even if the painting (which still has to be done by hand) is not very accurate. This is where the practical side of the hobby begins for boys (and girls too) if they wish to give their figures the correct colourings.

Several of the bigger manufacturers in the U.K. make series

of models in connection with national events, commemorative occasions, or for important films. In this way, the little figures become useful illustrations of a piece of history.

It is only within comparatively recent times that a serious attempt has been made to collect specimens and to record them for posterity. The Frenchmen D'Allemagne and Forrer were probably the first to realize their historical significance, and their example was so speedily followed that today there is a vast and world-wide body of collectors, all interested in the sometimes complex, and always fascinating history of the subject.

There is nothing wrong in playing with Soldiers. When Hans Andersen first wrote his story he called it "The Constant Tin Soldier". For "constant" is a word which means "staying the same". No matter what happened to him he was always brave and true and loving. Perhaps Hans Andersen was thinking of all the real Soldiers who came back from the wars and who in spite of their wounds remained cheerful and brave and true to themselves and their families.

PUBLIC COLLECTIONS

Toy and Model soldiers, ancient and modern, are prized by several museums throughout the world. In the United Kingdom collections are imaginatively exhibited in institutions which specialize in the plaything, and continue to add to their acquisitions, such as the Museum of Childhood in Edinburgh, Bethnal Green Museum and The Toy Museum, Rottingdean.

Many other national and military museums present model soldiers grouped to depict historical occasions. In one London Museum a series of "Battles Down the Ages" project history brilliantly in diorama and utilize 190,000 tiny pices to illustrate the Battle of Waterloo.

Below are listed some of the Public Collections to which a visit will be found rewarding: —

Aldershot. R.A.S.C. Museum, Buller Barracks (models in barbola by James Morrison).

Beverley. East Yorkshire Regiment, Victoria Barracks (two dioramas by Stokes and Greenwood & Ball). Closed for an indefinite period.)

Blenheim Palace. Collection of 728 Lucottes.) By use of a mirror backing an illusion of 1,500 massed troops is created.

Canterbury. Museum (one model).

Dorking. Museum (wooden automata).

Edinburgh. Scottish United Services Museum, Edinburgh Castle (Pilkington Jackson wood-carved statuettes: diorama of flats).

Regimental Museums of the Royal Scots; King's Own Scottish Borderers; Highland Light Infantry; Cameronians; Black Watch; Gordons; Seaforth Highlanders; Argyle and Sutherland Highlanders (plaster replicas of the statuettes by Pilkington Jackson in the S.U.S.M.)

Museum of Childhood. (See page 63) Collection in process of expansion.

Gateshead. Saltwell Park Museum (Coronation of Elizabeth II in Timpo figures).

Lewes. Anne of Cleeves' House, Sussex Archaeological Society (small collection of early Britain's: not on show).

Lichfield. South Staffordshire Regiment Museum, Wittington Barracks (Stadden). Wooden and cardboard cutouts illustrating history of uniforms, 12" high.

London. Bethnal Green Museum (few flats).

British Museum (archaic figures; medieval nef, etc.).

Imperial War Museum (diorama; models with figures by H. H. Cawood).

London Museum (small collection of civil flats; Britains; Haffner; heyde; conjoint tin; Edward VII's clock; model of Lying-in-State of King George V; not on show).

National Toy Museum (usually on tour; small collection Britains: Heyde; Ochel; trellis tongs; carved wood; papier mâché).

Royal United Service Institution—the Museum (Siborne's first form; Mond Collection of Lucottes (not on show); permanent display by members of the British Model Soldier Society).

Tower of London (Siborne's second Waterloo model). Various Regimental Museums.

Victoria & Albert Museum (medieval nef).

Royal Hospital, Chelsea. Fine set of uniformed figures by Helmut Krauls of Vienna.

Luton. Museum (small collection of semi-solids; flats; wood).

Oxford. Ashmolean (copy of Strettweg Idol Cart).

Rottingdean. Toy Museum.

Salisbury. Museum (one diorama).

Sandhurst. Military College (one Pilkington Jackson). National Army Museum. At least one case on permanent exhibition of toy and model soldiers.

Tunbridge Wells. Museum (Allgeyer; Lucotte).

Windsor Castle. Queen's Dolls' House—Britain's miniature soldier figures, in tiny boxes specially moulded to scale.

York Castle. Museum (wood; cardboard; flats; Britains; one diorama of Balaclava).

Pirbright. Guards' Depot. Two extensive lay-outs of toy soldiers used for instructional purposes.

IRELAND

Major H. Harris (see page 160) will be pleased to put collectors into touch with Mr. Judd of Blackrock, Co. Dublin who possesses the most extensive collection in the Irish Republic.

PRIVATE COLLECTIONS

In Britain, and overseas, many wonderful private collections exist—amassed over the years by males of all ages and with varying professional backgrounds. Not surprisingly, a majority consist of retired or serving officers and men of H.M. Forces, but soldier collecting is a true democracy of play and often, enthusiasts who in private life are clerks and merchants, artists, actors, and bank managers, are known to meet and exchange news and advice about their hobby.

Private collections are rarely placed on public view, unless on special occasions and in aid of a good cause. The best way of sharing this drama of the miniature battalions, is by joining a Model Soldier Society.

Many such groups exist in European countries and North and South America. Their estimated combined membership is over 100,000. That means on even a fifty per cent reckoning there must be some 50,000 private collections in these countries alone.

In England enthusiasts belong to a thriving organisation— The British Model Soldier Society, a body served by honorary officers. The Society concerns itself seriously with *models not toys,* but its members freely admit that the basic torso of many a toy soldier has been ingeniously transformed into a unique and entirely individualistic model.

In such consummate craftsmanship, as much as in the pre-occupation with military history, uniforms and war strategy, lies the appeal of soldier collecting.

The story of the British group is summarised below by its energetic Hon. Secretary who is always willing to answer queries by research students, specialists and interested laymen.

An important private collection of model soldiers is owned by English actor Anthony Quinn.

THE BRITISH MODEL SOLDIER SOCIETY

As a result of contacts being made through letters appearing in the Press, twenty-two collectors met at the "Rendezvous Restaurant", in July 1935, and founded the British Model Soldier Society. Today the Society enjoys a world-wide membership of 690 enthusiasts.

The Society is a non-commercial organisation existing solely for the asistance of its members in the furtherance of their hobby.

Through membership, a collector learns much in regard to painting, conversion, animation, soldiering, and the sources of supply of both models and information regarding uniform detail.

Meetings are held once a month at Caxton Hall in London, and also in Brighton, where competitions, exhibitions and discussions take place. Other meetings are held in the provinces by local groups of members, and once a year for the benefit of those members who cannot attend the London Meetings due to the distance factors, Annual Meetings are held in Manchester, Chard, and Northampton.

A magazine *The Bulletin* is published bi-monthly, and is received by all members, and we exchange publications with some sixteen Model Soldier Societies of various nationalities.

Briefly, the hobby is portrayal, in miniature, of the "Fighting Man" through the ages, and the Society can at any time stage an exhibition depicting the Soldier from 3000 B.C. to the present day. Great stress is laid on accuracy and authenticity of uniform detail.

Anyone interested in the hobby may join the Society, although we do not accept members under eighteen years of age. The Annual Subscription due every 1st January is Twenty-five shillings, for which a receipt and Membership card are tendered.

For further details write to the Hon. Secretary.

FURTHER READING

Many valuable reference books on the story of toy and model soldiers are extant; these may be found in bibliographies given in standard works.

Two outstanding books are by French authorities in the field, both illustrated, with fine photography, and colour plates. Recommended to the reader of French are: —

Figurines et Soldats de Plomb, by Marcel Baldet, with a preface by General Koenig, published by Editions d'Art Gonthier, of Paris.

Le Monde Merveilleux Des Soldats de Plomb, by Paul Martin (Curator of the Historical Museums at Strasbourg), and Marcel Vaillant, published by Editions Charles Massin, Paris.

*   *   *

These French writers are well-matched by two contemporary Englishmen, each owner of a remarkable collection and each author of an erudite and well-documented volume of great appeal to the general reader.

John G. Garratt is author of *Model Soldiers: A Collector's Guide,* published by Seeley Service & Co., 196 Shaftesbury Avenue, London, W.C.2, 42/-. The work, containing 240 pages, is well provided with an Index and Directory. The text is not only concisely arranged for reference, but well-documented with line-drawings. Photographic plates are of excellent quality. The text records the history of military and other miniatures traced from the earliest times through the Middle Ages and the subsequent periods of famous and much sought after masters of the art. Makers in almost every country are thoroughly classified and all that is known of their methods is recorded.

Considerable attention is paid to the modification and adaptation of existing commercial figures for special purposes or for uniforms or actions not otherwise attainable. Much attention is paid also to the actual casting or modelling of figures by the keen amateur collector, and to the building and arrangement of dioramas.

Mr. Garratt is a bookseller and may be contacted by enthusiasts and students of the subject at Sexton's Bookshop, situated near the G.P.O. in Brighton.

A recent book (1962), having a more popular appeal, though

written with great expertise, is *Model Soldiers,* by Henry Harris, (Weidenfeld & Nicholson, 128 pp. 27/6). The author has been actively engaged in work on the Royal Army Ordnance Corps' History, and while stationed at the R.A.O.C. School in Aldershot, found time during his researches to visit most of the collections previously mentioned. He is also familiar with private collections, being a staunch member of the B.M.S.S.

Many of the illustrations are taken from his own collection. These include not only single figures, but several panoramic displays of whole "armies", depicting scenes of warfare and ceremonial. In addition, there are models of artillery wagons and other forms of transport and armaments, drawn from the armies of many nations and several centuries, reproduced in accurate detail from the originals.

Major Harris tells how, as the son of a Cavalry officer, he began collecting model soldiers when he was a small boy. It was during the first world war, and his family lived in Aldershot. But, as the author makes clear, *that* one wasn't a "total war", and every time his father came home on leave he brought a red box of toy soldiers to his son.

By 1918, when young Harris and his mother moved to Dublin, his collection had expanded to over 500 figures of all arms and corps, and he recalls that he used to have reviews and mock battles with another Dublin boy, who had a collection of some three hundred. In these war games, he says: "I lost many irreplaceable models, but some of them were replaced by purchases from the Dublin shops."

SHOPS FOR COLLECTORS

The Sentry Box, 23 Beauchamp Place, London, S.W.3. (KEN. 1270.)

Hummel, 16 Burlington Arcade, W.1. (HYD. 7164.)

PART VI

MUSICAL BOXES AND MUSICAL AUTOMATA
MUSICAL AUTOMATA

The fantastic evolutions of these eighteenth-century Toys For Grown-ups delighted the Courts of Europe. They were the parents of our modern calculating machines. G. Bernard Hughes points out the surprising fact that their elaborate mechanism was based on scientific principles established over a thousand years ago. An illustrated manuscript, *The Book of the Knowledge of Ingemon's Geometrical Contrivances,* compiled in 1206 by the Arabian scholar Al-Jazari, describes the exact types of automata then known and includes several of his own construction, such as two dancing men and a strutting peacock. Drawings show these water-driven machines to have operated on principles no different from the earliest 17th century automata, and those of an even later date.

Until the early 18th century automata—with the exception of clocks, with which their evolution is closely connected—merely mimed, and were seldom accompanied by sound. These were usually constructed from gilded bronze. Typical were ladies dressed in farthingale and bodice, elaborately engraved and chased in brocade-like patterns. When wound, they moved forward, turned their heads as if singing, and gestured with their hands.

Toy Musical Boxes derived from the elaborate caskets of French and Swiss origin, sometimes made of gold or silver and encrusted with gems, small enough for a nobleman's silk pocket. They were first made about 1835. The earliest types were round metal boxes, fancifully painted. They played a single tune and were operated by a crank. As the market developed, popular demand became so great that not only were more and more novelties devised, but the mechanics of operation were improved as well. Unique features of a mechanical nature were developed, and soon people stood amazed and half-believing before birds that moved, girls that danced, clowns and acrobats that performed, and beautifully-gowned ladies who sat at pianos or organs emitting the most delightful music. A life-size canary was the delight of Queen Marie Antoinette, made by a Paris craftsman.

Musical movements have been fitted, at one time or another, to a variety of things—tankards, jugs, fruit-dishes and other unexpected objects which play on being picked up from where they are innocently resting. Fob-seals, watch-rings and scent-bottles were formerly designed with concealed musical movements to surprise the hearer and to challenge the craftsman to make ever minuter miniatures. Even the handle of a decorative fan, or of a useful umbrella or walking-stick, might have concealed a musical-box when this craze was at its height. Gold cases for sealing wax are also known. One of these rarities contained a movement only in inch and three-quarters in length, and little more than half an inch in width and height. It played a tune on five tiny bells.

Novelty-variants range from photograph albums of ample Victorian dimensions which, upon being opened, render tunes like *Home Sweet Home* or *Auld Lang Syne,* to cigar- and cigarette-boxes playing selections from comic operas and nearly-forgotten early musical comedies.

Several great composers did not disdain to compose music especially for musical-boxes. Haydn wrote a series of pieces to be played by three clocks that had been made to the order of his patron, Prince Esterhazy. Mozart wrote his *Fantasias in F minor* for an automatic flute. It is related that Beethoven was fond of hearing Cherubini's overture to *Medéa* as played on the musical-box in one of Vienna's cafés.

The more ordinary boxes play a wide variety of tunes—from operatic arias to folk-song arias. These tunes frequently give a clue to the date of manufacture. Unless ordered specially, the cylinders fitted into the boxes were always set with the prevailing pop-tunes of the day.

At the same time, tiny automated creatures were evolved,

made in gold and silver and set with precious stones. Skilled watchmakers catered for a rich man's market and created mechanisms for gem-studded golden caterpillars that crawled naturistically across a polished table; or for gold enamelled mice with golden tails and set with pearls that ran hither and thither with incredible speed, sometimes pausing to raise themselves before starting to run again; or, for jewelled frogs that croaked as they jumped or, most fascinating of all, for those tiny caskets which, at the touch of a concealed spring, released a bijou-like plumaged bird which turned and fluttered in an ecstasy of bird-notes and then, as suddenly, disappeared.

Birds have always been among the most popular of automata, right from the days when Vaucanson launched his fabulous duck on an excited French public. Catherine II, Empress of Russia, was presented in 1780 with a large caged mechanical peacock made by the English mechanician, James Cox. The peacock is now in Moscow. The miniature singing-birds were originally invented to go with snuff-boxes. They were, understandably, popular and expensive. Among the best-known makers of these remarkable *tours-de-force* dating from the late 18th, and earlier 19th, centuries, were the Jaquet-Droz Brothers. The most ingenious toy for grown-ups featuring a singing bird was a gold pistol from the mouth of which a tiny birds would mechanically emerge and sing when the trigger was pressed. Most of these have survived in the public collections of Museums, furnished châteaux and stately homes; or, in private collections.

Such a one, set in gold and enamel box and adornd with diamonds, was on show at the Great Exhibition, London, in 1851. It was bought by the mother of a Norwich meteorologist, the late Mr. John Willis, who bequeathed it to Norwich Castle Museum, where it now may be seen.

Singing Birds which were fairly commonplace about sixty years ago have acquired exaggerated value owing to their popularity with a growing number of wealthy private collectors.

Their rarity and market value fluctuate according to maker's mark and place or origin. *Country Life* reported (Aug. 25th, 1960) the sale at Sotheby's of a specimen made by Les Frères Rochat, for £920! Exquisitely and ornately designed in ormulu, and only one foot in height, the bird-cage dates from about 1820. It is described as "a beautifully made thing", with its twin Corinthian columns supporting an architrave at each corner of the octagonal platform. There are double doors at each side, and these and the domed top are formed of beautifully executed filigree work—foliage and arabesques. The clock in the base, quarter-striking, sets the bird singing at each hour, and a lever at the side actuates the bird at will. At the base of the dome, at each side, is a crown above a ribbon bearing the Garter motto, which encloses the initials A.F. These are probably of Adolphus Frederick, Duke of Cambridge (1774-1850), Field-Marshal, Colonel of the Coldstream Guards and Viceroy of Hanover from 1816 to 1837. The base is decorated with chased roses and thistles; the feet are lions' paws, and above them are acanthus leaves. The whole thing is as pretty a toy as one can desire.

No less ingenious was a small rectangular singing-bird and musical-box by the same makers, less imposing and only about three inches long, which would be taken for a normal snuff box at a casual glance. It was of gold with floral borders in blue enamel, with lid and base opening to reveal two compartments. The musical movement was operated by two knobs on the front; the singing bird, with its bright plumage, appears as soon as the lid is raised above a gold plate. When concealed, the bird is covered by an oval lid, with a Classical head in relief. This went for £800.

The musical-box enjoyed its heyday from 1800 onwards for about a hundred years. Its distinctive sound was then as much part of the home as radio or television is today. It is not remarkable that so many people have collected, or begun to collect musical-boxes of all types—from the large parlour models playing medleys in inlaid polished containers, to the frivolous toys and automata in which picturesqueness, movement and melody are all combined to divert the mind and intrigue the eye. Not only may we appreciate their fascinating melodies and *ambience,* but the craftsmanship that made possible such enjoyment has its devout admirers today.

SOME PRIVATE COLLECTIONS

The E. L. Oldfield Collection of Automata was meticulously built-up over the years at the home of its owner, a building contractor, at Thornton Heath, near Croydon, Surrey, It comprised a variety of modern tankards, jars, and similar souvenirs, mostly of twentieth-century make; some remarkable 19th-century tableaux, ranging from ships heaving on the ocean, equilibristes, monkeys, and several French items; 18th century singing-birds, watches, snuff-boxes, and finger-rings of gold. Mr. Oldfield, during his lifetime, went to Cairo specially to purchase some of the rarer treasures that went under the hammer when the King Farouk Collection was sold by the Egyptian authorities.

These, and other acquisitions, in turn went to the London auction rooms in 1956 after his death and when his widow disposed of the collection.

While in his possession the automata appeared on B.B.C. Television.

Also much in demand, a decade or so ago, by the film and television studios has been the collection owned by Mr. H. B. Steiner, of 4 Ashley Court, Frognal Lane, N.W.3. Mr. Steiner is famed as a Haute Coiffure Trichologist, and it was at his Grosvenor Street studios that a few of his pieces, like the Smoking Monkey (French, early 19th century), and the Kittens' Tea-Party, first attracted attention. He explains that he has now lost much of his initial interest in his automata, as "all the publicity, lending and whatnot", caused him more inconvenience than they are worth!

Some of his most interesting specimens appeared in a colour feature published by the *Illustrated London News,* and as illustrations to the first edition of *Children's Toys Throughout the Ages**.

*   *   *

The most important private collection of Musical-Boxes, large and small, was amassed by the late Mr. A. Pole, of Marlborough, who died aged 81, in 1962. Mr. Pole was a dedicated collector and had an immense knowledge. It was, therefore, a great disappointment to those interested in the subject when the collection was broken-up and sold. In 1949 the entire range was exhibited at the Science Museum where a list is, presumably, obtainable from the archive.

Most of the Pole specimens have dispersed to augment existing, or to start new, collections in various parts of the world.

*   *   *

Many examples of antique musical-boxes were the subject of a Lecture-Demonstration at the Science Museum, on 2nd January, 1962, given by Mr. Van Riemsdijk from whom details are available on request.

*   *   *

Another interesting assemblage was exhibited at Foyle's Gallery, Charing Cross Road, W.C.2, in December 1962. These came from the collection of Mr. Gerald Planus, the Thames Sewing Machine Co. Ltd., 254 Jamaica Road, S.E.16, from whom particulars are available.

This Exhibition also included musical-boxes owned by John Entwhistle, Esq. and R. Moss, Esq.

*   *   *

A few hundred yards from Foyle's Gallery, at 57 Greek Street, Soho, W.1, is The Juna Antique Shop, full of curios and fine period jewellery, bric-à-brac, china, dolls, and so on. A feature of the shop is the large musical-box in fine condition, which the proprietress is always willing to play for interested customers. Selecting gifts to such atmospheric music is not vouchsafed in many London shops!

* L. Daiken (Batsford 1952).

Mr. Bruce Angrave, 92 Dorset House, Gloucester Place, London, N.W.1, has made an intensive study of musical-boxes and mechanical musical instruments of which he is an enthusiastic collector. He has lectured and broadcast on this subject, with particular reference to Polyphons, (ancestors of the phonograph and gramophone), and the giant parlour version of the Autoglockenpolyphon.

* * *

The Windsor Collection, accommodated at 14 Park Avenue, Leeds 8, Yorkshire, is possibly one of the finest in Britain today. Rare and precious Singing Birds and miniature *objets de vertu* comprise its greatest part, for Mr. Winder has been collecting all his life and has the highest standards and fastidious taste.

* * *

The J. H. Barnett Collection of Musical Automata and Singing Birds are accommodated at the private residence of the owner, a retired automobile engineer living at The Grotto, Tettenhall, Staffordshire.

Mr. Jack Barnett has devoted many years to his hobby and this remarkable assortment of antique musical-boxes and automata were the subject of an illustrated article in *Country Life* (December 6th, 1962), for whose kind permission to quote, to the editor and the owner are given.

Most of the 70 or 80 automata were in a state of dilapidation when acquired by Mr. Barnett, who restored the mechanisms and dress to their original condition with contemporaneous material over a period of several years. It is Mr. Barnett's wish that his collection should find a permanent home as a gift to a sponsored organisation, provided that suitable conditions can be agreed.

In a popular series of domed cages issued from the late 1830s gilded brass bars rose from a mahogany base enriched with gilded metal and measured about nine inches in height.

Japanned cages with attractive colours painted with floral ornament were made in Wolverhampton from the late 1840s by Edward Perry, of Temple Street, Henry Fearncombe, of Dudley Road, and others. The metal base containing the mechanism was spun in a single piece and fitted with a thin sheet-iron cover. The sides and dome were of wire passing through there flat rings. These inexpensive cages were sold to toy makers, such as Evans and Cartwright, of Wolverhampton, who completed them with birds and mechanism from the Continent.

Leafy *bocages* protected by a glass dome might contain several humming birds hopping backwards and forwards from one branch to another in exactly the manner of real birds confined in a cage, flapping their wings, moving their tails, turning their heads and opening their beaks. There was also a continual chirping, apparently kept up by the birds. The levers that carried them backwards and forwards were concealed in slits cut in the artificial branches.

An unusual example embowers four singing birds, three flying from branch to branch, one drinking from a shell and another from a pool. Some bear the label of Charles Bontems, established in 1849 at the Rue de Clerry, Paris. Bontems, who won a gold medal at the Great Exhibition for his collection of bird automata, had simplified the mechanism, the eight cog wheels operating the birds' whistle being reduced to two worked by a spring barrel. The *bocage* generally rose from a papièr mâché base shaped and coloured to represent grass and lichen-covered earth with low branches for the birds and pieces of mirror to simulate pools. The mechanism was concealed in a shallow box below.

THE MUSIC BOX GALLERY

Collections of this *genre*, as we have observed, come and go; their owners pass away and a life's work and knowledge are dispersed to enrich other or newer private homes, or are lent to public Museums by bequest.

But we have in London a living link with past and present

PLATE XXVIII

*An exhibit at the Guards Brigade Museum, Pirbright, being used for instruction
in the ceremony of Trooping the Colour*

[*Photo, Alan Meek*]

PLATE XXIX

"Little Wars". (*See p.* 153)

PLATE XXX

Soft Toys by Maud Cranfield. (See p. 227)

PLATE XXXI

"The Rocking Horse". (See p. 188)

[*Photo, Antony Panting*]

Soft Toys by Helen & Rosemary Julius

Plate XXXIV

Creations by Sam Smith. (See pp. 221-223)

Plate XXXV

PLATE XXXVI

Wooden Toys by Susan Wynter. (See p. 230)

[*Photo, John Banks*]

PLATE XXXVII

PLATE XXXVIII

Unusual creations by Doreen Masterson. (See p. 229)

PLATE XXXIX

PLATE XL

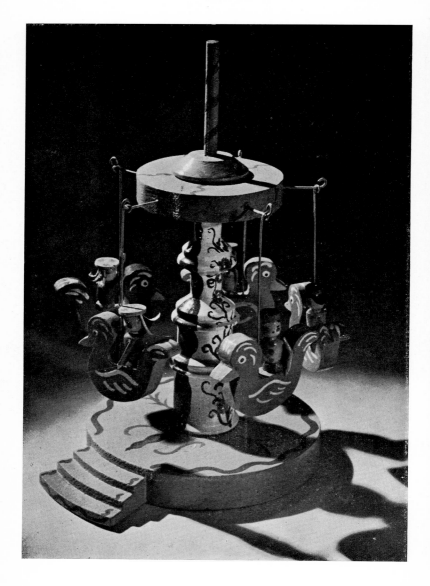

A 7″ high Roundabout by Yootha Rose. (See pp. 223-224)

devotees of automata—a man of exceptional erudition and mechanical skill. Mr. S. F. Sunley comes of three generations of Swiss craftsmen in the musical-box trade. He has in his unique shop—know to every English owner who has had to get a specimen repaired professionally—a bewilderingly varied collection. It comprises some of the very earliest French, German and Swiss automata inherited from his father and grandfather; Jumeau-dolls fitted with musical movements; singing birds in cages and in caskets; modern musical-box novelties; all these—filling the shop like a scene from *Petroushka* or *Coppelia* and rubbing shoulders with other automatic dolls, acrobats, elephants, or swans in for repair, and bearing their owner's names on tie-on labels.

His new gallery is part private museum, part workshop, for it is more spacious at its present location at 81 George Street, Portman Square, W.1 (not far from The Classic Cinema, Baker Street) than was his smaller apartment at 1 Park West Place, Marble Arch, from which the accumulating toys virtually drove him for lack of space!

Mr. Sunley, a fund both of technical knowledge and historical data relating to his unusual craft, keeps all his treasures in repair. The Clocks tick-tock; the dolls and animals frozen in silence, with their lifelike expressions seem to wait for the magic hour of midnight for a turn of keys to set them all dancing, trapezing, miming, tinkling, cuckooing to a phantasmagoria of organ-music, bells and birdcalls!

During his career as restorer, he must have had dealings with every known collection, public and private. He has a remarkable memory for detail, and can recall exactly which French quacking duck went where; and which Chinese tumbler went elsewhere. He is always willing to talk about his subject, inspect other collectors' pieces, and help the serious student with facts and figures. But if he does not feel disposed to share his secrets about how to make damaged figures live again, who can blame him? For he must surely be the last of the traditional Curiosity Shop people—in whose eagle

169

eye and slight accent are vested the know-how of the great mechanicians of Middle Europe who made the House of Hapsburg gay and oriental potentates gasp in wonderment. In the upstairs workshop rooms at his house, he has about 150 pieces—the majority of them all unique; all of them working properly. Some are as big as a small wardrobe; others are no bigger than a snuffbox. Most of them are more than a 100 years old. Quite a number of the pieces stand under their permanent glass domes; others are carefully shrouded in silken covers, the more minute musical-boxes lie snug in display cabinets.

Mr. Sunley does not just look at them, or show them off to charm the visitor's eye, he likes to see the figures on them moving rhythmically and to sit and listen, and dream to their individual tunes. He hopes his visitors have the same idea. The late Queen Mary saw and heard these antique treasures, and was most interested in their history. The Queen and Prince Philip have also studied them and listened to their tunes. Collectors from all over the world have sought out the workshop and been allowed to look at and sometimes play them. They have offered hundreds of pounds for various "pieces". Mr. Sunley just smiles apologetically at such offers, regrets they are not for sale. But suggests perhaps he has something similar which might be found attractive. To the most persistent he explains shyly that he is thinking of a museum for "them".

The years roll by in these workshop rooms. Some of these musical-boxes have a tinkling tune, pure of note but light as gossamer. Others have tunes whose notes are as deep and as reverberating as organ notes. There are two "pieces", which in their own right are models of craftsmanship and history, stand as centre-piece. One has a figure nearly three feet high with a matching box as base. The other is like a small dolls' house, carved in ivory. The latter holds the eye at once. Mr. Sunley as he fondles it, says quietly and happily "It was Franz Schubert's, the great composer." It was his inkstand.

You see the hollow for the sand, the well for the ink, and the rest for his quill. It is an exact miniature reproduction of his house in Vienna, and was presented to him in 1825 by his devoted friend Johann Michael Vogel. Mr. Sunley turns a hidden key and the notes of "Ave Maria" float sweetly from it. The other much larger "piece" has a perfectly sculptured Pierrot clad in yellow silks. He stands graceful and smiling with hand resting on a chair. When a key is turned a gay tune begins. The smiling Pierrot slowly begins to move and soon he is performing the most lifelike hand-balancing feats on the chair back, matching the tempo of the music. "It was made in France more than a 100 years ago by a family which has made musical-boxes nearly as long as my family. Many have wanted to buy it, but I keep it for my museum."

Surrounding these two pieces are a Swiss harmonium musical-box with a brightly-plumed bird which hops and flies from branch to branch in time with the tune. A bird organ with its handle to turn to teach canaries, finches, humming birds, and so on, to sing from its tutoring. A Negro flower girl with her tray containing a monkey, a dancer and a mouse, with everything moving when the tune plays; an elephant playing a hurdy-gurdy with its trunk and not forgetting to beat the drum with its tusk; a small church reed organ found in a Norfolk church which plays hymns at the turn of a handle.

Some of these pieces have always been in Mr. Sunley's family. Others he found in his searchings. Some he got from collectors. (They know me and they come because they know their treasures will have a good home, just as any one looks for a good home for their dog or cat, and I always give a fair price.

But Mr. Sunley does not just live in the past, some of his latest musical-boxes have tunes from "My Fair Lady" and "West Side Story". He is too, very proud of the musical-box he designed for the coronation. It resembles a miniature portable television set, contains 35 mm. film, giving six pictures on the screen of the Queen, Prince Philip, the coronation coach, Buckingham Palace, Westminster Abbey, and the Houses of Parliament. It plays "God save the Queen". Thousands of these Coronation musical-boxes have been sold all over the world, especially in the Commonwealth.

Mr. Sunley says, musical-boxes are gaining more popularity every year. People like them because of their pretty tunes, because they are romantic, maybe because they bring back the past. "I think if I get my museum it will be very popular, too."

TWO PUBLIC COLLECTIONS

BIRMINGHAM CITY MUSEUM AND ART GALLERY

THE DEPARTMENT OF SCIENCE AND INDUSTRY, NEWHALL STREET, BIRMINGHAM, 3.

Open: *Mondays to Fridays,* 10.30—5.30.
Saturdays, 10—5.30.
Sundays, 2—5.30.

This is one of the most representative Public Collections of Musical-Boxes in Britain. They are mainly large in size and are catalogued. Reference lists are available from the Department on request.

The body of the collection at the moment is concerned with mechanical organs of the barrel type, hand-crank-operated. In this category there are six, all but one of which date from the end of the 18th century. The odd one is a street organ of 1886 by Thibouville of Paris.

There is a Steck Pianola, an Organista, e.g., a stringed instrument operated by keys from book-form music. They have an Aeolian Orchestrelle (116 note tracker action reed Organ, operated from paper rolls). There is also the Blackpool Tower Orchestrion Organ by Imhof & Mukle (1879).

172

There are three disc-type musical-boxes, a Synphonion and a Polyphon. These are of the common penny-in-the-slot type with about 14"-diameter discs. The third is a small table model with 6" discs.

Other exhibits are at Singing Bird Clock and a Black Forest Organ Clock of 1815.

In addition, there are two cylinder type musical-boxes of the common type, dating from about 1875. These have eight tunes per cylinder and were made by Dawkins of London.

The collection of Phonographs and early Gramophones is also a representative one.

THE PITT RIVERS MUSEUM
PARKS ROAD, OXFORD.

Open: *Weekdays, for students, 9—5.*
for general public, 2—4.

The Pitt Rivers' Collections form an integral part of the University Department of Ethnology and Prehistory, the present and past of the same subject. The collections are not in the main arranged by areas, but by subjects, to illustrate the origin, development, geographical distribution, and variation of some principal arts and industries from the earliest times to the time of their mass production, or to explain technical processes in them.

The Collection was founded by General Pitt Rivers in 1851 at Bethnal Green, and began with a study of the history and development of firearms, which he afterwards extended to cover many other subjects. It next moved to South Kensington, and was given by the General to the University of Oxford in 1883, with the provision that a separate annex to the University Museum be erected to hold the collection and subsequent additions, and not used for any other purpose.

The musical-boxes are not on show for the public. Their nature requires the private rooms, and they can be occasionally demonstrated during vacations and by appointment only.

The boxes are housed in the Curator's room as they need an even temperature, and can be seen by appointment only, since it is impossible to allow general access because demonstrations require the presence of a knowledgeable person, and most of the Museum staff are engaged in teaching. The Curator, Mr. T. K. Penniman, however, is always ready to oblige the serious visitor and researcher, if contacted in advance.

It is to him that I am indebted for much of the information about the Collection.

"A rare and very early Waterloo Box presented by Mrs. Symons in memory of her son. Many of these were chosen from the Symons' Collection shortly before the death of the late Mr. A. J. Symons, who was greatly interested in our plan to illustrate the history of automatic music as a part of our collection of about 5,000 musical instruments from all parts of the world.

"The Waterloo Box, as its name implies, was made about the same time as the Battle was fought, and is one of the earliest examples of the musical-box independent of the watch or other small object to which the music was incidental. It belongs to the class of instruments known as linguaphones, in which the graduated metal tongues of a comb are plucked by pins of a revolving metal cylinder parallel to it, and driven by clockwork, instead of being plucked by the fingers or thumbs, as in the African Sansa, their prototype.

"We have the table Regina with 9-, 15-, and 19-inch discs; the Stella, with 17-inch discs; the Three-Disc Symphonium, which plays three discs at once; the 24-inch Polyphon; and the interchangeable Regina, which picks up and plays any one or more of a dozen discs from its carrier in the order desired.

"Among automata in a different class, we have two cages of singing birds, which work by square-toothed wheels against levers and plungers that shorten or lengthen air-columns in tubes and thus produce a variety of notes. Toothed wheels working on levers and threads make the birds move. We

174

altogether lack the miniature examples of singing birds in little boxes and on tinder-pistols, and the musical watches which preceded the musical-box, or were contemporary.

"Other pieces of the cylinder type in the Museum are the Table-Grand, Sublime-Harmony, Forte-Piano, Harp-Piccolo, Orchestral, Revolver, and Double-Cylinder. The Table-Grand, Orchestral, and Double-Cylnder have extra cylinders which can be inserted, and the last named plays two cylinders at once in harmony. Sublime-harmony has three combs, the upper with a delicate bell-like tone; Forte-Piano has a loud and soft comb; and Harp-Piccolo has two combs; the Orchestral has a wind-organ, percussion drums, and other effects added; and the Revolver changes from one cylinder to another by raising a lever attached to a wheel on which the cylinders are bolted, a leved which must only be used when the machine is at rest. The best cylinder boxes were made by Nicole Frères or other Geneva makers, and according to Mr. T. G. G. Bolitho, the dates can be ascertained from the first two figures of the five-figure numbers on the machines or their programmes, the *Gamme* numbers referring to their repertory. The Ste. Croix makers, of whom Paillard, and Paillard, Vaucher, Fils are best known, took out patents for their Swiss inventions in the United States of America, and Mosoriak has listed the dates of patents in that country. Of miniatures in the cylinder class we have only one first-rate one by Rochat, and none by such makers as Bordier. Among automata, we have a Turkish Dancer, lent by Mr. J. M. Thompson, in which the music-box cylinder is geared to a wooden drum with pins, levers, and threads to work the figures. There are also the usual pleasant oddments like musical fruit-stands, scent-boxes, albums, etc."

To the foregoing Notes compiled by the Curator may be added to the following half-dozen entries chosen at random from the Card Index to give a further indication of the Collection's range and scope: —

(a) Miniature Musical-Boxes 4″ × 2″ and 4″ × 2½″.

(b) Singing bird in black ebony-type casket, French make.
(c) Autophone, English.
(d) Mid-Victorian clasp-type photograph album consisting of 16 board pages and musical unit fitted into back cover.
(e) Symphonium.
(f) Polyphon: Mus. B. brought to England 1860-70. Plays two tunes, one being the Overture to Weber's *Oberon* (late 1820s).

There are interesting photographic records also available for inspection.

A MISCELLANY OF MUSIC BOX AND AUTOMATA THEMES AND ACTIONS

A mechanical doll, white wig and holding hoop, to right of unit, motions to a yellow duckling who nods his head, to fly through the hoop.

A clown seated on a musical-box plinth plays a mandoline, strumming action of right hand.

Peacock walks and pauses occasionally to display its tail.

A tambourine player beats his drum, pirouettes and kicks his leg to ring bells.

Monkey dressed in 18th century costume, bewigged, plays a harp.

Monkey in similar costume powders his nose, takes snuff.

Monkey, same period, puffs smoke from a cigarette when lighted and placed in his paw.

Bootblack, while rolling his eyes, and dancer perform movements to music.

On musical-box plinths are a trio of period dolls—a tambourine lady; a conjuror; a violinist.

A 19th century automaton costume doll, porcelain face, powders her nose and moves a gilt hand-mirror with the other hand.

Victorian doll pianist seated before upright piano, flanked by miniature potted plants, moves fingers over keyboard to music.

Musical-Box in the form of a golden Welsh Harp, playing four tunes, formerly in the late Queen Mary's Collection.

Boy doll violinist (right) plays instrument, while girl doll danseuse (left) pirouettes in time.

A ballerina with a blue "tu-tu" goes through formal positions to music, on a velvet-covered plinth.

A monkey violinist (left) accompanies another dressed as clown lying on his back, and rotating a ball on his feet (right).

Child with a toy theatre containing a trapeze acrobat. When the curtain falls, the small white dog in the basket waves farewell.

Red velvet easter-egg opens to music to reveal head and pink eyes of a furry white rabbit. Closes again.

Boy doll leaning against lamp-post (right) serenades girl in Swiss national peasant costume. The box has a panoramic Alpine view to the front.

Humorous automaton: while the butcher tries to stop the pig from entering the sty, holding its tail fast, the butcher's feet clatter on the hollow plinth.

Mechanical bear, with real fur, wearing circus cap, taps on drum.

Mechanical bear walks, growls and opens its mouth.

Mechanical tiger walks and turns head to the side and opens jaws.

Mechanical elephant, walks and moves trunk.

Mechanical bear pours real water from a bottle in right hand to a beaker in left, and drinks.

Mechanical writer, made by Frederich von Kraus in 1760, actually writes on a sheet of paper.

Juggler plays with discs or spheres.

Acrobat balances himself on hands, turns a somersault and repeats.

Group of Indian acrobats in tableau perform tight-rope and other tricks.

Nightingale, humming-bird, finch or canary, in gilded cage bursts into song, moves head, opens beak and flaps wings.

18th-century silver model of Swan by Weekes, London, now in Bowes Museum, Barnard Castle. To accompaniment of music, the water, made from barley-twist glass-rods, appears to ripple and flow. The swan reaches down its head in an attempt to catch some fish swimming in front of it. 67" in length.

Vista of ship on ocean and train crossing bridge linking castle to house. To accompaniment of music the sailing vessel rocks and the train moves.

Vista, seascape. Contains a musical box and the ships in foreground toss to the motion of the waves.

FOR FURTHER READING

Les Automates, by A. Chapuis and E. Droz (Neuchatel, 1949), is the standard reference work on this subject.

Other books containing valuable information for the collector or specialist are: *Mechanical Musical Instruments* by Dr. Alexander Buchner, and with an English translation by Iris Urwin (Batchford Press, London), has some very fine colour reproductions. Earlier works of reference are *The Curious History of Music Boxes* by Roy Mosoriak (Lighter Publishing Co., Chicago), and *Musical Boxes* by John E. T. Clark (London, 1952).

Encyclopaedic references appear in *The Oxford Companion to Music* by Percy A. Scholes, under the heading "Mechanical Reproductions", and *The Concise Encyclopaedia of Antiques,* Vol. II, under the heading "Automata".

An interesting publication is the well-documented catalogue in French of the finest European public collection on record at the Musée Du Conservatoire National Des Arts Et Metiers, Geneva, when during September-November, 1954, superb examples from many countries were exhibited.

It is entitled *Horloges Et Automates.*

PART VII

WHERE TO BUY INTERESTING TOYS
SOME SHOPS IN, OR NEAR, LONDON

1. CONVENTIONAL TOYSHOPS
2. FOR ANTIQUES AND PERIOD PIECES
3. TRICKS, JOKES, PUZZLES, NOVELTIES
4. TOYS OF THE NATIONS
5. SHOPS WITH SPECIALITIES
6. EDUCATIONAL PLAYTHINGS

Hamley's was established in 1760 by one William Hamley who came to High Holborn from Bodmin, where he set up in business with "The Noah's Ark", has besides a long trading history, literally everything of interest to the toy-buying public within the orthodox range. A month before Christmas season it is usually jam-packed with young and old.

The shop's Managing Director, Mr. J. S. Pullin, knows the toys business backwards and has prepared for this compendium a special review of the 1963 trend, as follows: —

"In the past 15 years the British toy industry has made such giant strides in every kind of toy that well over 90% of our stocks are British made.

"We do, of course, also sell the best of the foreign novelties from all over the world.

"The most successful toys are faithful models of the real things of life and every year they get more advanced.

"Electric model Railways, Roadways and Car Race Tracks; Scientific Toys—Weather Forecasting Stations, Radio Sets and Radio-controlled models; Dolls and Teddy Bears that actually speak many different sentences; Pedal Motor Cars and Sports Cars in truly modern design; the old clockwork novelties have given place to battery operated ones; but there is still a sale for old favourites such as the Rocking Horse.

"Similarly with games. All the modern T.V. panel games are here, but so, also, are Ludo, Snakes-and-Ladders, and Happy Families."

Mr. Pullin's wide knowledge of the toy field is always at the disposal of the correspondent who has a query, or who seeks something unusual.

Of the large Departmental Stores, Selfridge's of Oxford Street have a long-established reputation, largely the work of an energetic and imaginative buyer, Mr. Loveland. Apart from the run-of-the-mill lines, you never know what surprises turn up on their counters—fantastic Japanese or German-made automata (clockwork-powered); traditional British or other playthings; and, every Christmas, imported toys and dolls rarely seen throughout the rest of the year.

Indeed, the policy of Selfridge's, Liberty's of Regent Street and, in 1963, Fortnum & Mason (Piccadilly) to mount special displays of foreign toys before Christmas have enriched the experience of Londoners, and particularly of toy collectors. A few years ago Selfridge's presented for sale an excellent range of Japanese folktoys, including character-dolls, paper toys, tricks, bamboo novelties, toy lanterns, miniature wall-masks and plaster or *papier mâché* items. The range, so colourful and exotic to the general public, became popular and now a summer exhibition is also held.

Liberty's discerning toy buyer often mounts delightful folk-toys from Japan, including lathe-turned "talking" dolls of solid wood which squeak by manual action, and lacquered dogs, which also make attractive ornaments.

*　　*　　*

Woolland Brothers, Ltd., of Knightsbridge, have in the past run two outstanding toy Exhibitions; one of Japanese play-things and ephemera in October, 1960; and another, of Mexican toys in February, 1962. For Christmas, 1962, they ran a novel international toy display as part of their "Gifts From All the World" promotion.

In addition to a variety of well-chosen folktoys from many

lands, Woolland's stock exclusive lines in strikingly coloured soft toys and, with a theme throughout the Department like "Toys With An Adult Appeal", the originality of the Store's approach can be guaranteed!

*　　　　*　　　　*

British buyers, apart from the specialist shops, have been slow to appreciate the wealth of prototypes made in countries with long traditions, like Asia and the South American continent. From the latter examples of Mexican and Peruvian objects, beautifully and decoratively conceived in baked clay or other natural materials, are being seen more frequently of late.

For Christmas, 1962, Fortnum & Mason staged a fine collection of toys from Peru which attracted much interest and, thanks to importers like Primavera, Ltd. (see page 193) this relatively untapped field is becoming still more widely explored.

*　　　　*　　　　*

The Toy Department of Heals, Tottenham Court Road, W.1, specialises in well-designed toys from all over the world. From Great Britain a number of craftsmen produce special hand-made toys of excellent quality and design; wooden toys like trains and tugs by John Gould; soft dolls with charming faces and beautiful dresses by Elizabeth Stevenson; rag dolls and cuddly animals, both large and small; hobby-horses with soft heads covered in gay fabrics, and a variety of others. From manufacturers come a selection very carefully chosen, e.g., sacks of bricks, constructional toys, puzzles and games. Nests of dolls from Russia; an ingenious rattle from Denmark; cane prams for dolls from France; willow-pattern tea-sets and paper umbrellas in bright colours, from Japan. Books for all ages are a speciality.

Many new toys are always being added to the range, and some of the old ones leave to make way for changes. As craftsmen make individual articles, it is often not possible to repeat identical toys and it is always preferable that a customer should choose the one that is most to his, or her, liking. The shop, noted for its contemporary furniture and furnishings, was founded over 150 years ago.

* * *

Riché, the House of Haute Coiffure at Hay Hill, Berkeley Square, devotes half of its ground floor space to toys for sale in an *ambience* of carpeted, Mayfair elegance. Their specialities include beautifully-made toy horses, and it is their claim that the craftsman who turns out these animals will copy faithfully any small owner's horse or pony! The range includes hunters and hacks; working horses and draft animals; pony-and-trap and a delightful pony-and-sleigh. Perhaps the most attractive is the Drum Horse, popularised by parades of the Household Cavalry.

The Maison Riché soft-toy animals range from Persian cats to kitties in most realistic fur, to Pekinese cocker-spaniels and poodles (in naturalistic or caricature designs), good traditional teddy bears of many makes; humorous animals; and, an all-wool original porcupine that is ideal for toddler and pre-school ages.

The shop is proud of a series of miniature mice, made of felt, dressed in exquisite detail (like Racey Helps *Barnaby*)—Mister and Missus, nursemaid, and children—obviously the work of an artist dedicated to perfection rather than production. They have amusing things imported from Italy, notably bunny-rabbits—one sleeping on its inseparable cushion.

Standard stocks include a good variety of souvenir and character English regimental figures, Beefeaters, and so on.

* * *

Cats, in every way comparable in elegance and daintiness to the Riché mice, are made by Lydia de Quincey, who runs a charming arts and crafts shop at 4 Kensington Church Walk, W.8 (behind St. Mary Abbot's Church). This series is ceramic, tastefully designed and dressed, is hand painted, each cat with an individual personality, as Mrs. de Quincey's artistic training was as a potter.

In listing some of the larger London retail stores it would be a mistake to overlook those pocket-sized Boutiques and Galleries dotted over the metropolis, wherein the patient shopper may discover some eclectic or fascinating plaything made or supplied solely by the owner. A few of such places are recorded under SPECIALIST SHOPS on the succeeding pages (206-9).

Mention here, however, must be made of The Otway Toy Studio, at 41 Knightsbridge, S.W.1, which is probably the smallest shop in London, but which has, nevertheless, a good stock of fine hand-carved toys. Mrs. Otway supports British creators of hand-crafted toys and is the only person selling elm-wood miniatures by Stanley Noble (from 2/6). Stocks, always variable, include John Gould's superbly made wooden railway trains. (*See page* 228).

The Stonehenge Woollen Industry have three well-known shops in the West End of London specialising in handwoven tweeds and hand-knitted jerseys, cardigans, etc. Having had a long association with goods made from pure wool, the management has encouraged the sale of soft toys made by craftswomen within the industry.

Thus it is a common sight to Londoners familiar with the firm's tasteful window-display to see delightfully-conceived birds and animals in gay colours perched about the fine fabrics!

These soft toys are ideal for small children, but many collectors prize them because of their individuality and realistic design. They include the following specialities, normally in stock, but easily obtainable to order, if not: —

Birds: Robin redbreast, bullfinch, blue-tit.

Animals: Fleecy lambs, rabbits, tortoise, Siamese cats and kittens, elephants (felt), and teddy-bears (plush).

Animal Families: Novelties of exquisite diminutive workmanship include hedgehog family and ladybird family, ranging in size from a half-crown to a sixpence.

The shops are situated at: 18c Grafton Street; New Bond

Street, W.1; 69 Welbeck Street, W.1; and 8a Sloan Street, Knightsbridge, W.1.

SHOPS FOR ANTIQUE AND PERIOD PIECES

I always make a point of reminding those professional Museum people whose good fortune it is to sort out and arrange for display splendid collections presented or bequeathed to this or that Museum, that if it were not for collectors they might be unemployed!

This salutary remark is intended not so much to denigrate the fussiness or irritability of those officials who like to pick out the plums from a collection (relegating to the storeroom or basement what must have given pleasure to the donor), as to make allowances for the eccentricity and obsessive qualities which many collectors develop. Collecting is no plain-sailing matter. As soon as a serious collector becomes expert in a narrow field, he realises the vastness of his ignorance. To this realisation add the fact that the field of toy-collecting is now becoming as cluttered almost as the Doll territory; objects are scarce; dealers pay, and expect, more; and the almost maniac drain on our British heritage by American dealers and collectors has spoilt the joy of the chase with a neurosis resembling tension more than a sense of adventure.

Be that as it may, collectors are necessary, desirable and completely praiseworthy. Though many fine collections (more's the pity) do get broken up, changing hands as individual pieces or in lots—though valuable ones often come under the auctioneer's hammer—a good proportion are donated, or willed by a bequest, to our public institutions to become part of Britain's collective heritage.

By the same token, collectors depend on their own private sources. A majority keep in contact with shops or connoisseurs and often, in a funny way, with quasi-criminal evasiveness. Rivalry stimulates as in all connoisseurship.

Gordon Hand experiences the unpredictable, like most antique dealers. Invited one day to inspect some Ming porcelain in an English country house, he was confronted by 140 period dolls, lying about on tables and chairs! It was a genuine hierarchic collection, starting with dolls of Queen Anne's day, and passing down the same family, with more dolls representing every generation, played with, cherished, and always preserved.

He noticed that moth was present in the trunks which accommodated them and, on an impulse, bought the lot from the two maiden ladies—last of their line. The "doll-collecting itch" had attacked him, and within a few months he had reached the hundred mark and decided to give an exhibition in Kensington in aid of the Red Cross.

He was informed that the late Queen Mary, a keen collector and connoisseur, wished to visit the Exhibition. She insisted on going round the exhibits twice, taking careful note and on leaving she presented him with an autographed copy of her book about her own Dolls' House at Windsor. That visit bestowed on Gordon Hand the melancholy honour of being the last dealer whose shop was to receive Her Majesty's patronage.

Through his hands have passed fabulous collectors' pieces as well as everyday playdolls of all kinds. He specialises in miniatures and Dolls' House accessories and furniture—ranging from the 1720s to the 1890s, sometimes gets a period Dolls' House (though these are becoming much harder to come by due to the collecting craze) and bric-a-brac of juvenile interest.

Among the items he has offered to collectors here and in the U.S.A. have been Talking Dolls, Walking Dolls (Auto-Peri-Patet-Ikos) and rare prototypes in china, *papier-mâché* and vulcanised rubber—with characteristic hairstyles. He tells me that he was once lucky to find in a junk shop a contemporary descriptive pamphlet, dated 1885, recording the full and hitherto unrecorded story of the House of Jumeau, manufacturers of the most-sought-after Paris Fashion Dolls. As a result of his discovery the publication has been reprinted privately in the U.S.A. The impression conveyed of that thriving business is fascinating. It employed 350 skilled workers in the factory, sometimes 30 on a specific assembly process, and their turnover reached well over a million francs a year.

*   *   *

Another dealer with expertise in period dolls is Eveline Butler, who has a welcoming shop in the heart of that antique mart, the Portobello Road, W.11 (Number 91). In her own words is here given a brief description of her interests: —

" As you know, anything interesting and unusual attracts me and the infinite variety and ingenuity shown in the making of dolls and toys, from the very sophisticated French Jumeau dolls and mechanical toys to the Regent Street penny toys and the carved wooden dolls which are so much a mirror of the man who made them as of the things which they portray are the sort of things which I like to deal in, and so as not to lose sight of them entirely when I sell them, my husband is making a colour film of all the most interesting ones.

"There are also the educational toys and games, such as praxinoscopes, jigsaw puzzles, card games and such like things of which the variety is infinite, as well as the elegant trifles made by young ladies, such as superb pedlar dolls, of which, alas, many poor imitations have been made, some of them very recently. The list can be continued indefinitely, but I hope that this will give you an idea of my activities."

*   *   *

BAYLEY'S GALLERY, 9 Princes Arcade, S.W.1 (off Picadilly), specialises in *objets de vertu;* prints and pictures; china and glassware, mostly quaint. They concentrate also upon miniature furniture and china for dolls' houses; apprentices' pieces; and *recherche* Victoriana which fuse the plaything and the absurdity. Here the collector may hit upon an unexpected treasure. The stock comprises: model soldiers; dolls; old games; tables games and *papiers de fantasie;* juvenile drama; greeting cards with juvenile themes, e.g., Christmas and Valentine cards; scraps, music-sheets.

From time to time are offered for sale toy saving banks;

tin toys and automata; shells and flowers under glass; bird-cages with amusing birds; card-cases, needle-books and pin-cushions. Curios ranging from a Nailsea glass ship to nine tiny tables on a 6″ board, may greet the eye and the Proprietor, who is in touch with many collectors, is always willing to try to track down some elusive *objet d'art* for the discerning customer.

A water-colour painting of Bayley's Gallery by William Gaunt is on view in this small but fascinating shop.

*   *   *

Easter eggs were first conceived as playthings for children and, happily, still retain something of this origin in the toy world. The more sophisticated cariants, like the enamelled and bejewelled eggs made by Fabergé for the Tsars of Russia, have assumed the zenith as collectors' treasures. They are now essentially antique "Toys for Grown-ups". The House of Wartski, of Regent Street, W.1, is a specialist in the field, and their Mr. A. Kenneth Snowman is the author of *The Art of Carl Faberge* (Faber), which is a standard reference book, finely illustrated.

Another antique shop where they have a good reserve of porcelain Easter Eggs is M. Eckstein Ltd., of 90 Jermyn Street, W.1.

*   *   *

THE DOLL SHOP, at 15 Moscow Road, Bayswater, W.2, is known to children and collectors far and wide. It represents the life ambition of a collector and enthusiast, Miss Irene Blair Hickman, who is a retired physiotherapist, preferring to run this unique establishment to practising her normal profession.

An active member of The Doll Club of Great Britain, former Hon. Secretary of the British Toymakers' Guild, and co-opted as a Trustee of the Toy Museum, Miss Hickman's knowledge and expertise regarding dolls are sought by collectors in many lands, by film and promotion people and the general public.

Being first and foremost a dedicated collector and scholar in the field, Miss Hickman prefers not to part with her treasures and her private collection, on view in the shop, are of dolls that may entice the would-be purchaser but which are permanent fixtures!

In her workshop on the premises, Miss Hickman makes dolls and dresses them to order in any style. She repairs expertly damaged or broken dolls, replacing parts with authentic substitutes, a skill that ranks her Doll Hospital among the last surviving establishments in the Kensington area.

Her private collection is rich in graphic material on themes of dolls, toys and play, comprising storybooks, old prints and engravings, photographs, scraps and cut-outs.

Treasures from The Doll Shop are loaned for Exhibitions and for Television, but most of all for the many good causes and Charities in West London with which the owner is associated.

*   *   *

Another shop which draws toy enthusiasts magnetically is THE ROCKING HORSE, at 23 St. John's Wood High Street, N.W.8. This address has become the centre of a revival in period rocking-horses, an attachment to childhood which shares in British life the same nostalgia as for teddy-bears. Seekers after genuine old rocking-horses, repaired and put into clean, gay, working condition, need journey no further than this shop with its charmingly arranged window full of period toys and dolls, and interior that spellbinds. It has an interesting story.

Some ten years ago a few friends were talking about the difficulties confronting young people obliged to earn their living in dull offices and at mechanical trades, and have their artistic outlets frustrated. They decided they would like to encourage such people by offering them an opportunity to work at crafts and develop techniques of various kinds. Accordingly, a form of Artists' Guild was set up and this resulted in the opening of the Rocking Horse toyshop.

It took its name from the lively trade which grew around the public demand for "real" rocking horses that parents and grandparents knew in their own childhood. The team of crafts-workers, preferring real-hair manes and tails to rubbed substitutes, began again where the (now defunct) carvers and toy-makers of Lines Bros. left off, before World War II. Leather workers make by hand the delicate harness and the comfortable saddles, artists with a sense of design re-paint the restored models in cream, dappled grey, black and other gay colour combinations. They favour vivid rockers instead of the old-fashioned brown-varnish finish.

And so The Rocking Horse and its clientèle has grown, and each year works at full pressure months before Christmas to cater for waiting orders. It has now drawn into its orbit Victorian playdolls and, arising logically from this, the sale and restoration of dolls' houses, furniture, dolls' clothes and accessories. Nineteenth-century and Edwardian toys are a speciality, and one need have no fears about sending a cherished item here for repair.

* * *

CUMBERLAND ROW ANTIQUES, of 41 Camden Passage, London, N.1., CAN 0643, although ostensibly specialising in ceramics, usually have antique children's toys, games, dolls and books tucked away, and since the proprietors are themselves collectors, they always enjoy meeting others.

ANNUAL ANTIQUE MARTS

Collectors of period pieces will find that many antique shops keep some of their finest treasures for exhibition at one of the annual Antique Fairs organised by the trade. These are listed below and, apart from the satisfaction of making personal contact with dealer-specialists, and obtaining useful information there is always the opportunity of coming across examples of peiod dolls, toys, table games, children's books and ephemera, music boxes, singing birds and dolls' house accessories ranging from fine silver miniatures to ivory, porcelain and polished wood.

ANTIQUARIAN BOOK FAIR

In conjunction with the National Book League, held at the League's Headquarters: 7 Albemarle Street, London, W.1. (in '63).

THE ANTIQUE DEALERS' FAIR

Grosvenor House, Park Lane, London, W.1. (Usually 12 or 13th June, for about two weeks.) Organising Secretary: Captain C. S. Platts, Grosvenor House, Park Lane, London, W.1.

BRIGHTON ANTIQUES FAIR

Organised by the same committee as Kensington Fair. (In '62, held 11th-21st July.)

CHELSEA ANTIQUES FAIR

Held spring (in '63, 8th-18th May); and autumn (in '63, early October.) Organising Secretary: Mrs. Josephine Grahame-Ballin, Antique Dealers (Exhibition and Organisers), Ltd., 21 George Street, St. Albans, Herts.

KENSINGTON ANTIQUES FAIR

Held Kensington Town Hall. (In '62, 30th August-13th September.) Miss Beryl Davy, 34c Kensington Church Street, London, W.8.

MIDLAND ANTIQUE DEALERS' FAIR

Held at Solihull Civic Hall. (In '63, 23-27th April.) Chairman of Organising Committee: Mr. A. I. Silvester, Warwick Road, Solihull, Warwicks.

THE NORTHERN ANTIQUE DEALERS' FAIR

The Royal Hall, Harrogate. (In '62, 13th-20th September.) Chairman of committee: H. Tweed, Esq., Messrs. J. & W. Tweed, 408-410 Leeds Road, Bradford 3, Yorks.

SCOTTISH ANTIQUE DEALERS' FAIR

(First held 1963, 30th April-3rd May.) Adam Rooms, George Hotel, George Street, Edinburgh. Chairman of committee: P. J. Williams, M.B.E., T.D., Propert Williams, Ltd., 36 Victoria Street, Edinburgh 1.

An arcade devoted entirely to Antique Dealers and their wares is situated at 42 The Broadway, S.W.1 (opposite St. James's Park Underground Station). Tel.: WHI 7997. Known as "The Westminster Antique Galleries" it is a venue for collectors and gift hunters, open daily Mondays to Fridays, 10.30—6 p.m. There are forty firms installed here.

* * *

Visitors to Britain unfamiliar with the trade can receive lists and specific information from The Antique Dealers' Association, 31 Wood Lane, W.12, also from the Editor of *The Antique Collector* Magazine, 16 Strutton Ground, S.W.1, and the Editor, *Antique Dealer & Collector's Guide,* 92 Fleet Street, E.C.4. *The Antique Finder,* a monthly magazine magazine devoted to current auction prices including a collector's guide and classified advertisements covering "Wanted" and "For Sale".

FOR TRICK-TOYS; PUZZLES; JOKES; NOVELTIES; MAGIC AND MASKS

One of the sad casualties of the changing face of post-war London is perhaps the disappearance from High Holborn of Ellisdon & Son, a store with a worldwide reputation for toy novelties and jokes, the largest mail-order house in the world for conjuring and novelties, with a catalogue which todays fills one with remembrance of things past.

Not entirely past, however, for new shops have arisen to fill the gap created by the closure of that famous firm. One of its contemporaries, L. Davenport & Co., of New Oxford Street, is still very much in business, run by the daughter of its famous founder and newly established opposite the British Museum at 51 Great Russell Street, W.C.1.

Here, alongside the old favourites in the world of Magic that we knew at Christmas parties for children between the Wars, are the very latest tricks and puzzles. Although Davenport's are, traditionally, famous for Magic, and supply books and equipment for Magicians, they carry a large stock of the more amusing novelties, and all the amazingly new theatrical masks in rubber materials.

Famous for three generations, having been founded in 1898, Davenport's stock and service are outstanding in the field. They will also recommend or provide Magicians and entertainers for children's functions.

Among the items in their current catalogue are the following: Japanese wooden puzzles (spheres and cubes); Invisible ink; rubber plate-lifter; tin with three snakes; magic bottle imp; Chinese finger trap; jumping snakes; dehydrated worms that expand in water!

*   *   *

Another centrally-situated Trick and Puzzle shop carrying a wide range is Messrs. Williams, 13 Tottenham Court Road, W.C.1.

*   *   *

Hamley's, Ltd., and Messrs. Heal's have a Magician's Counter widely patronised by professional and amateur magicians.

Equally well worth a visit (or communication by letter) is THE MAGIC AND FUN SHOP at 104 Shaftesbury Avenue, W.1. This "small shop with the giant collection" is owned by Tommy Cooper and enthusiastically managed by Mr. A. Alan, who is perhaps the only shopkeeper in London who greets customers with a trick sword thrust right through his scalp!

Here again one will find the conventional and entertaining things, half-joke half-plaything, which give endless fun during leisure hours. They offer up-to-date duplicated lists, and these include: Japanese puzzles; ring puzzles; "Tipsy Joe"; King Tut (miniature mummy in a coffin); quivering spider; flik-flik magic picture books, magnetic toys like dog-and-ball, footballer, Jack the Magician, and kissing dolls, giant comb, toothbrush and biro-pen; flasha wool; whizz-bangs; mock sugared almonds and trick sweets; vanishing cigarettes; water toys like squirting bell-pushes; exploding toys like matches, pen, cigar; spring-operated toys like snake camera; frightening novelties like skeletons, realistic grass-snakes, pop-out snakes, etc.

They also carry a large stock of funny and character masks.

ORGANISATIONS

Entertainment Magicians for children's functions may be contacted through: —

THE MAGIC CIRCLE. Secretary: Peter Newcombe, M.I.M.C., 38 Overdale Avenue, New Malden, Surrey.

THE INTERNATIONAL BROTHERHOOD OF MAGICIANS

(The British Ring No. 25).

Secretary: W. G. Stickland, "The Wand", Ferndown, Dorset. Tel.: Ferndown 2444.

TOYS OF THE NATIONS

PRIMAVERA, LTD., a craft shop situated at 149 Sloane Street, S.W.1 (the Sloane Square end), is reputed for its exquisite and tasteful offerings. The Management, pledged to a distinctly personal standard, has for a number of years built up a clientele for the highly personal toy. It may be useful, it may even be played with, but *chez Primavera*, what counts is that it has a strong personality of its own *that makes you want to possess it*.

Their range appeals more to grown-ups than to children, or to be more anthropologically correct, "to the child in every integrated adult". They were first to launch as a Toymaker catering for the living-room or the studio more than the play-room, that remarkable artist-craftsman, Sam Smith. (*See page* 221), whose work may always be obtained here. His boats are so alive, whether they be dinghies, seagoing tugs, sophisticated yachts, or just essays in surrealism. The voyagers are usually old salts, jack tars, substantial females, toughs, softies, aunts, uncles and horrible children—a seafaring *Comedie Humaine*!

Smith loves people—he creates toys evocative of beach scenes with bathing belles; peep-shows fantastiques; mobile mood indicators of unthinkable ingenuity; splendid rugged lions; sleek horses, ravenous tigers or placid cows—each, like an individual painting or piece of sculpture having a maximum of vitality.

Primavera has an extensive range of imported folktoys; traditional softwood villages and whittled trees from East Germany, where the time-old peasant skills are still encouraged; from West Germany, Austria, Sweden, Denmark and Japan come toys with national characteristics. There are unusual animals and birds of terracotta from South American countries; lovely construction toys from Switzerland and Finland, and carved wooden toys and character figures with an individualist design from Israel. Each Christmas sees something entirely unexpected, while the variety of exquisite Christmas Tree ornaments and surprise decorations, is an annual delight.

A short descriptive list of items from Primavera include these: —

1. TOYS

Germany. Building bricks in natural and painted wood in X shape for easy interlocking construction—can almost be used as a puzzle toy.

    Musical boxes with toy-like tableau, handmade in wood and paper.

Finland. Trot, Hip and Mushroom—small whimsical creatures made in leather, felt and fur. Some are dressed in miniature, traditionally printed Marimekko dresses.

    Fenma house in softwood. Basic Finnish dwellings to be built from interlocking wooden logs in the kit.

Japan. Hand carved wooden toys, on wheels, gaily painted in grasshopper, cricket and insect shapes.

England. Woven wicker rattles with small bells inside.

Norway. Wooden buildings, houses and shops. Can be made up into villages and towns. They are hand painted in bright, typically Scandinavian colours.

2. DECORATIONS AND MOBILES

Germany. Christmas Tree stars made in symmetrical shapes of straw and reeds. Tinfoil angels, for Christmas decoration in traditional mediaeval shapes and colours.

Free moving mobiles of wire and aluminium foil in shapes based on natural motifs—multicoloured "tropical" fish, birds and fir trees.

Switzerland. Glass, three dimensional star shapes for Christmas Tree decoration.

3. ORNAMENTS

Italy. Hand carved wooden horses—very typical of primitive, Italian peasant art.

Switzerland. Three glass pigs, one inside the other.

Peru. Retable wooden chest, brightly painted with ceramic altar attached to inside of box.

Huge church in natural colours—a potter's interpretation of the church in Quinua.

One plaster procession—Cuzco, Peru; represents a religious procession in the streets of Cuzco on a Saint's Day, including street vendors, policemen, tourists, etc.

*　　　*　　　*

But five minutes stroll southwards from Primavera, at 89 Lower Sloane Street, Pimlico, S.W.1, is the newest of London's chic craft-shops. It is called MEXICANA and is run by a company, of which the Managing Director is a young Mexican artist knowledgeable in the workmanship of his native land, Alfredo Bourdet.

Mexican folktoys have an intensity and a quality all their own, appreciated by collectors and travellers, familiar with these. They specialise in terracotta pieces of vivid beauty like those nursery candlesticks designed in the Tree of Life pattern; bamboo birdcages, finely-wrought, each with its toy bird inside. Here you may well hope to procure those fascinating "death" toys ("Muerte con aplicacion de volante") known at popular Mexican fairs and fiestas, featuring skeletons in frivolous situations, and made of a paper base. Horsemen and birds made of plaited cane or grasses are another traditional *genre* peculiar to the country—all vivid and dramatic and enjoyable.

Fantasies in baked clay and inexpensive brightly-painted wooden toys include: boxers, snakes, native birds, miniature chairs and kitchen dressers, with price ranges from a shilling to a pound. A marvellous lot of clay whistles or money-boxes of the earliest (and possibly the first-known) designs, birds, horses, fish, etc., upwards from seven-and-sixpence each.

Señor Bourdet will offer you, among his standard lines, white paper doves and brightly coloured paper flowers such as Mexican children adore; cocksure-looking cockerels made of tin; Christmas decorations in the form of flying fish, whistling birds, lanterns, and lustrous stars, all from half-a-crown upwards—and a unique line in Christmas Trees.

Although the shop features serious products in wood, glass, ceramic and metal, there is a light-headed atmosphere due entirely to the juvenilia, so tastefully displayed there.

*　　　*　　　*

The Scandinavians are particularly good at handmade toys in a variety of materials, and the most exciting display of these may be seen throughout the year (but particularly before Christmas) at the store, No. 95 Regent Street, W.1 (the Austin Reed end), known as DESIGNS OF SCANDINAVIA.

From Denmark the late Kaj Bojesen produced an enchanting collection of animals in solid wood—monkeys, bears, rabbits and elephants. Lions made from rope, and reindeer sledges in paper, and fir cones, are just two examples from a wide range of imaginative toys by Danish craftsmen.

Also made by individual craftsmen in Sweden and Denmark are fascinating mobiles, the best of which are probably those in straw. Trolls, those mythical creatures from the mountains, hand carved in wood, or in fur and cloth and constructed from wire, are both frightening and amusing.

All in all Scandinavian toys are unsophisticated, designed to appeal to the imagination of the young and, by the same logic, to grown-ups, who are enthusiastic about this shop.

*　　　*　　　*

TIVOLI, of 223 Brompton Road, Knightsbridge, S.W.3, shows a wide selection of Scandinavian merchandise, including delightful toys and clothes for the child up to three years. Toys include simple wooden bell cubes, circular wooden rattles/teething rings, gaily coloured wooden soldiers with moveable joints, 9″ high; and animals from Denmark.

Unusual idea for the nursery wall are the Danish wall-hangings, handprinted on cotton in bright, gay colours: guardsman with real fur busby, $17\frac{1}{2}″$ x 10″.

*　　　*　　　*

CZECHOSLOVAK HANDICRAFTS, of 45 Oxford Street, London, W.1, have always in stock an attractive selection of large and small dolls in a variety of regional costumes; animated sports figures; carved wooden animals. Easter eggs painted in traditional designs and, in pottery, piggy banks, miniature slip-ware jugs and hand-painted bird-whistles. They also have a selection of unusual "pop-up" fairy tale and animal books and other attractive children's books.

From time to time, dolls made from maize-straw, puppet-dolls, wooden flutes, dolls' furniture and wooden toys and bricks are available.

*　　　*　　　*

At 195-197 Regent Street, W. 1, there has opened recently THE GREEK PRODUCE DISPLAY CENTRE. Its latest introduction to the West End shopper is a variety of conventional toys made in Greece. But together with the more orthodox lines comes a pleasant surprise for the collector of costume-dolls. Greek national costumes still survive as being among the most varied and colourful in Europe and since almost every island, village and remote hamlet clings to its sartorial tradition, the regional costumes adorning these dolls are always hand-made and extremely colourful. The villages and islands weave their own cloth and the dolls themselves are a reflection in miniature of the workmanship and beauty of their lovely costumes.

The Manager of the London shop has contributed the following details about some of the costume-dolls in stock and if these, or others are not available all the time, orders are placed and speedily delivered: —

North Corfu. Over a simple long undergarment, trimmed at the hem with ribbons, is a graceful dark dress, lined with material in two colours. The skirt is lifted at one side and fastened to the waist, thus creating a variety of colour and also a very practical pocket. A very brief bolero covers a white blouse with very full elbow-length sleeves, and a white headdress is worn draped from the crown of the head. A necklace of several chains, decorated with coins is worn.

Attica. Threads of real gold are used in the heavy and extensive decoration of the wedding dress of Attica, which has a very elaborate skirt and short coat, reaching to the finger-tips. A long silk scarf is draped around the head with the ends hanging at the back, over this is a small coronet type ornament with a row of gold coins arranged over the forehead.

The ordinary costume of Attica has a long silk skirt of brocade woven with gold or silver thread, a dark bolero embroidered at the edges, with long full sleeves, again displaying at wrist and neck the fine white blouse. A small flat fez-type hat is worn with this dress.

Sarajatsana. This is a dress worn by wives of some nomads of Greece, and has a sleeveless bolero and skirt of dark material, richly embroidered. White blouse with very full elbow-length sleeves with cuffs from the wrist of the same dark coloured embroidered material. This is again repeated on the dark stockings. A dark headscarf is worn, and heavy gold chains crossing over the breast, and which date from the revolution days.

Macedonia. This is a comparatively simple costume, of a calf-length white dress with embroidered apron and three-quarter length fitted coat, both of a dark material, a wide belt woven with a silver thread, again the white blouse with lace cuffs showing beneath the coat sleeves. Gold chains and coins at the waist and neck of this costume and a small headdress is worn by single girls, while the married women wear a hat black with feathers and based on the helmet of Alexander the Great.

Patmos. The attractive ensemble worn by the women of this island has, for a great many years, charmed visitors. The long silk broad-striped skirt has two rows of heavy fringing around the lower part of the skirt. This fringe also decorates the lower edge of the just-below-the-waist length bolero in a dark material, displaying at the wrist and deep horseshoe shaped neckline, the white blouse.

A hat, rather similar to a tall cossack, heavily embroidered and draped wimple-fashion with a long silk scarf.

*   *   *

Almost nextdoor neighbours to the Greek Dolls is another centre for unusual handiwork from the Balkans. This is the YUGOSLAV SHOP at 193 Regent Street, W.1.

Here is assembled from all the regions of that country a fine assortment of embroidered work, carved wood items, ornamented leather, ceramic, fabric and glassware. Dolls are particularly varied and Costume-dolls in three sizes (45 cms., 20 cms. and 12 cms.) represent no less than eight districts—Sumadija, Bosnia, Petrinje, Konaulje, Hercegovina, Somadija, Okolina, Beograda and Bitolj. They are outstanding in design and finish. There is also an amusing lot of solid wooden dolls—caricatures of rustic types; two sizes of elegant Sestina Costume-dolls; Greek dolls and figurines portraying peasants grouped with their mule, or shepherds with their flocks.

This is the only London shop where one may obtain, so

far, primitive toys of Greek design in delicate-toned terracotta —there is an archaic bull, a bird-woman, an idol, bear and bird, all similar to playthings unearthed from thousands of years B.C. This range is rough-finished. Glaze-finished Yugoslav variants consist of a bird-whistle, horse-whistle, and money-box in the form of a mythical bird—all equally attractive to collectors.

Wood is used imaginatively by Yugoslav peasants and the purchaser has a choice of different genres. There are expensive and artistically handcarved pieces in walnut, e.g., a sitting hen on a nest which serves as a trinket box, and an ornamented shepherd's flute of great beauty. A less ornate shepherd's pipe of a different type of wood makes a more suitable toy for younger children. There are softwood Weather Houses from the northern region, reminiscent of pre-war Austrian toys, with their little man and woman appearing as the barometer changes. From the same source comes an unusual set of odds and ends, called *Pedlar's Pack*—a delight to any youngster. This consists of 20 miniature domestic utensils, big enough for a very large Victorian Dolls' Kitchen—basket, sieve, barrel and wooden spoons, rolling pins and so on. Another series of Slovenian folk design is known as a "Posy from Ribnica". This is a set of wooden kitchen utensils, even smaller, and varnished—which makes them seem more ornamental than to be used in cookery games!

Analogous to the "penny toys" of fifty years ago is a range of popular wooden whistles, all made of bright yellow-coloured limewood, and with a character all their own . . . whistles in the shape of a cello, a bird, a flute, a hammer and a toy pistol.

Quite on its own is the Yugoslav traditional hay-rack, under its straw-thatched top, with a cockerel perched on top. While for the family which favours children's dishes on the table there are artistic egg-cups of painted wood. Another product of the Yugoslav Handicraft Shop are slipper-socks for children aged 2-11, leather soles and woollen tips—not strictly to be played with—but it is those of this place makes one enlarge on any intended gift rationing!

*   *   *

Of all the Slavonic toymaking peoples, it is gratifying to see that the Russian toy industry has been revived on a firm basis and its products have given endless pleasure to children and grown-ups alike during the past five or six years.

It is perhaps paradoxical that in countries that boast of individualism and private enterprise toy manufacture has swung away from craftsmanship into a mass-produced sameness, without character or jollity, whereas in a totalitarian state where, we are persuaded, all originality is quashed to a terrible and impersonal dullness, most of the toys now being made are in the strict line of peasant woodcarving and colour sense.

Side by side with modern conventional toys of a distinctive Russian quality (e.g., horses that neigh and dolls that cry), a wide range of Russian folktoys may be found constantly in stock at THE RUSSIAN SHOP, 278 High Holborn, W.C.1. These naturally include the nest-of-dolls, one fitting inside the other, from great-grandmother to infant, known as *Matreoshkas* and which, toy historians reckons, are symbolic of the life-cycle. A new variant is the *Swaying Matreoshka,* a most entertaining detachable doll, made of polystyrene, in the form of a kerchiefed smiling Russian woman, who nods her head and swings her full skirt by a clever balancing principle.

There is a splendid array of Costume Dolls, well designed in the peasant dresses of the Ukraine, Lithuania, Latvia, the northern regions and, of course, the Oriental styles of the East Soviet Republics like Uzbekistan, Tadjikistan and what used to be Tartary.

The wooden toys of movement are remarkably original and fascinating. Many feature the Russian Bear (Mishka, as he is known to Russian children), who symbolises the great primitive force of nature. Made in Borodskoye, he is seen pitting his strength against a peasant, or trying to outwit a wily fox.

A recent variant of this whitewood series has Mishka using the telephone!

Traditional scissor-movement toys like the shepherd and his flock, also come out of modern Russia, unchanged in 100 years or more. Lacquered wooden ornate boxes and dolls' house furniture are here, too; and carved wooden ornaments and figurines with a toylike quality. But the newest and most attractive line in the Russian Shop is possibly the series of 15 small dolls made of pressed cotton, beautifully proportioned, each dressed in a different national costume from within the 15 Republics of the U.S.S.R.

In the current catalogue are: *Pressed Cotton Dolls* and *Swaying Matreoshkas* and *Pyramids*. A large range of wooden painted toys, which can be taken apart and put together again in different shapes and sizes. *Nested Dolls*: Wooden nests of dolls, the mother holding several babies inside. Sizes available are 2 in 1, 3 in 1, 4 in 1, 5 in 1, 6 in 1, 7 in 1, 8 in 1. *Sounded Toys*: A series of toys giving realistic sounds of animals, e.g., miaouwing cat, barking dog, etc. *Mechanical Toys*: A range of toys with clockwork mechanisms, e.g., train set, airport with flying aeroplane, road junction, etc.

A few paces eastward from the Russian Shop one is surprised to find yet another handicrafts centre with a similar tradition, namely THE BULGARIAN SHOP. Here, also, is to be seen a wide range of folk-art objects, with the emphasis on lacquered wood, inlaid sometimes and always identifiable for its peculiar style. There are folkdolls and character dolls in fabric—perhaps the only examples of those dressed in authentic peasant national costumes of Bulgaria available in Britain. Ornamental crafts, novelties and souvenirs are more in evidence than toys of the *Miska,* fox-and-duck, or jumping-jack series made in Russia, but there is a good range of well-constructed kindergarten and pull-along toys.

ISRAEL is a new country and for this reason its toys are so far without any age-old tradition. Nevertheless, the fusion of western ideas and eastern craftsmanship has produced some original and distinctive playthings. (*See* PRIMAVERA *range, page* 193). THE ISRAEL SHOP IN LONDON LTD., situated at 76 New Oxford Street, W.C.1 (near the British Museum), stocks a limited range of character dolls representing Israeli types, e.g., Halutzim, Yemenites, and young people dancing the popular *Horah*. While it stocks dolls of mainly souvenir appeal, the shop can, if requested, obtain items of greater interest to the doll-collector. They have a playing card speciality, The Bible Game, colourfully illustrated, and a series of miniature U.N.O. trucks and other vehicles made of moulded metal.

The Italian Institute for Foreign Trade, 31 Old Burlington Street, London, W.1, carries a wide range of Italian traditional toys and games, together with costume dolls from all the Italian Regions.

Folktoys from India have a colourful and primitive quality. Whereas they are known to the layman mainly through the range of turbanned soldiers in painted and lacquered wood, and a few birds and animals, nowadays numerous traditional variants are to be seen in many toyshops. The popularisation of the sale in London of Indian playthings is due to two reasons: a fillip to the village craftsmen in India itself, who are encouraged to make toys for the world market; secondly, to a trading enterprise, INDIACRAFT LTD., of London and Paris, which has introduced the public to delightful examples.

This firm has a well-stocked shop near Marble Arch at 533 Oxford Street. Other London branches are at 254 Kensington High Street, W.8, 20 Bute Street, S.W.7. There is also a branch at 58 Henley Street, Stratford-upon-Avon.

Here one may buy animals, birds and playdolls of baked clay; wooden bird-whistles, finely wrought Kalighat toys from Bengal; elephants, horses and mystic animals on wheels, cast in polished brass; regional playdolls and costume dolls ranging from the delightful Bengali penny wooden "bazaar" dolls (all in one piece) to Thakki and Rajasthani ornamental figures and dancers from Manipur. There are cocks, owls, and pecking-birds, horses, camels, elephants representing different traditions—all new and exciting to English eyes.

Whatever the changing supply happens to present, one may be certain of coming upon the unusual and the artistic— ox-and-carts from Southern India; varnished cow-and-calf from Banaras; the delicate mayurpankhi, or peacock-boat; terracotta doll-shaped candle-holders for taking lights for the Diwali children's festival; sometimes puppets and marionettes; and almost always oriental instruments and hide-drums. As worthwhile as anything mentioned so far are the baby-rattles of superb design and as gay as one can find anywhere in the world.

*   *   *

Since Hong Kong and Shanghai have more active links with the British and world toy market than has China herself, it is inevitable that the former and not the latter will supply the shops long established in London. Only the tenacious searcher will exhaust the variety of Chinese toys to be found in London, for many curious and unexpected items are to be found in shops off the beaten track—strange and beautiful birds-eggs, hand-painted and mounted in toylike glass cases in a Chinese barber's shop in Monmouth St.; traditional mounted soldiers of baked clay, miniature wall-masks, paper toys that are artistic among modern inventions, birds-of-paradise, peacocks and other brilliant creatures made of chenille, at COLLET'S CHINA SHOP in Great Russell Street, W.C.1.

Wherever one goes in quest of the delicate products of Chinese skill, there will always be rewarding finds at THE ARTS AND CRAFTS OF CHINA, at 89 Baker Street, W.1. They import mainly from Hong Kong, but for years have their exclusive lines in Chinese playdolls (boy or girl models), paper parasols, children's fans and lanterns, china miniature animals, carved curios of all kinds, and always a favourite with the Chinese toy enthusiast, paper flowers that blossom like magic when placed in a glass of water.

The well-known series of softwood carved character toys—ploughman and bullock, cormorant fisherman, rickshaw-boy, water-carrier, and so on—are easy to find. They are stocked by the shop just mentioned as well as THE HONG KONG EMPORIUM, 53 Rupert Street, W.1, and THE GREAT WALL RESTAURANT, 33 Oxford Street, W.1, which has a department selling handicrafts and fancy goods.

At The Emporium a unique atmosphere prevails, and it resembles so much an eastern bazaar and so little a shop in London that one cannot resist reproducing verbatim a list of items offered : —

Windbells (strips of glass which tinkle in a draught).

Chenille birds, canaries, parrots.

Water flowers.

Plastic dragons.

Paper lanterns, small or large, for trees.

Various ornaments suitable for making ornamental gardens (bridges, pagodas, tortoise, fish, ducks, frogs).

Thermometer on stand.

White glazed dogs, $2\frac{1}{2}''$.

6″, 8″, 10″ Dolls in theatrical costume in plastic case.

The Great Wall Restaurant has a lot of Chinese bric-a-brac not found easily elsewhere. These range from chenille birds to porcelain animals (horses, ducks and other poultry); glass peacocks, clay pagodas, ornamental miniature wall-masks, and soft toys of many kinds. Perhaps the most unique sample of ephemera is their coloured bookmarker made in Wenchow, having a strong juvenile appeal. These come in paper envelopes in the shape of coloured *Leaf-blades* (i.e., leaf-skeletons in English parlance) which are fragile but durable and tie on to objects as well as mark a page.

Other charming bookmarks for children's presents sold here are of hand-painted Chinese silk.

SHOPS WITH SPECIALITIES

HORSES AND PONIES

At 18 Beauchamp Place, London, S.W.3, are sold realistic replicas of British horses. The animals are wired and can be made to stand or take up action position. Portrait copies of your own horse or pony are undertaken; or of your dog or cat.

At the workshops the prospective customer may view a wide range of models, new ones constantly being made so that the list is ever growing. Visitors are welcome and usually leave with a few attractive items for a child rider.

Average height is between 4½″ and 6″, and the finish is very good indeed. You can have an Arab stallion, a heavy carriage horse, a lightweight hunter in the act of trotting or gallop; and ponies galore—Welsh Mountain, Connemara, or Exmoor. These are foals and finely-made tack, including hand stitched leather saddles with adjustable girths and stirrup leathers; bridles with metal bits and coloured browbands; horse rugs with coloured borders and initial and leather roller; wooden gates for horses to jump over! . . .

Not forgetting hounds; they have foxhounds, hunt terriers and otterhounds. And to complete the play-pattern for offspring of hunting families—they have also walking fox, running fox and sitting fox; otter with fish; owls with baby owls.

*　　　*　　　*

CATS IN COSTUME

Lydia de Quincey's Studios. (*See page* 182).

SOLDIERS

*　　　*　　　*

Regimental replicas and models at THE SENTRY BOX, 23 Beauchamp Place, S.W.3. Collectors' pieces, model soldiers and souvenir-type figures at HUMMEL'S TOYSHOP, Burlington Arcade, Piccadilly, W.1.

EATON'S SHELL SHOP

Situated beside Foyle's Bookshop at No. 16 Manette Street, Charing Cross Road, London, W.1, they import from Africa, the Pacific and the Far East unusual craftwork and object of natural beauty.

This shop specialises in what must have been among the first natural playthings in human history—as still found in primitive island communities to this day—sea shells of all kinds.

Of a large variety recommended as children's toys, the following are always available: —

Cowrie (30 varieties).
Cameo, a red orange helmet shell.
Foxhead, beige-white.
Mitra, orange-red, heavy, smooth.
Pearl Order, irridescent, silver-green.
Pearl Oyster, irridescent, rainbow.
Pearl Snail, irridescent, white-green.
Pearl Trochus, irridescent, rainbow.
Pheasant, smooth, many-patterned.
Shark-eye, brown-beige, smooth.

A published price list, with sizes, is available on request.

Of particular value as a play-activity is their *Shell Collections* in display boxes, each shell named and laid out, with an appeal that is educational without appearing to be so.

Within the same marine context, this shop stocks other charming objects, such as sea-horses, starfish, blowfish, sea-urchins which in themselves must delight as well as instruct.

Among formal toys are offered the following unique lines: —

Baby Rattles made from coconut (Trinidad).
Hand-carved rattles in the form of a doll's body, with attractive faces at each end (Nigeria).
Wooden playdolls, hand-carved (Nigeria).
Kenya dolls (East Africa).
Calabashes (gourds from East Africa) with pips inside that make amusing percussion toys.
Maori dolls (hand-carved, rare) from New Zealand—periodically in stock.
Beads of all sizes and colours, wooden and glass, for threading, games, decorations and beadwork.

Microscopically tiny hand-carved elephants (about $\frac{2}{3}$mms.), which fit into a small hollowed-out red bean (from Ceylon).

* * *

REGENT JEWELLERS LTD., 93 Regent Street, London, W.1., supply exquisitely made Dolls' House miniature candelabra, coffee-pots and other silverware.

* * *

MATERNELLE BABY BOUTIQUE, at 199 Sloane Street, Knightsbridge, S.W.1, is a speciality shop for babies and has a good range of "toys to love". Teddy bears and bunnies are pastel coloured; small, soft and safe enough for the youngest baby.

* * *

THE EVA HAUSER GALLERY, of 281 Finchley Road, Hampstead, N.W.3, was one of the first shops in the country to specialise in good modern design for the home. This standard has been maintained in the selection of toys, which are excellently designed and functional.

Local craft is represented here by The Toy Trumpet range of wooden toys, hand made with skill and ingenuity by Susan Wynter; from a simple colour wheel for the very young, rising and falling Maypole, nursery and Christmas tableaux, to the more ornamental and sophisticated designs for charming, entertaining little men with their handcarts.

Exclusive to this shop is a selection of toys from Switzerland, including a wooden Baby-clock, colourful wooden counting men, zig-zag constructional play-bricks and pillars and satin-smooth, carved and polished wooden toys.

Also a good selection of tiny wooden toys, including trains, from Scandinavia.

* * *

HAND-PAINTED SHELL EASTER EGGS

Made by Polish traditional artists, and known as *Pisenki*, for Easter, orders are taken at ORBIS LTD., 38 Knightsbridge, S.W.1, and CZECHOSLOVAK HANDICRAFTS (*see page* 197).

POLLOCK TOY THEATRES
Replicas of original Pollock Toy Theatres, juvenile drama sheets and kindred material at 44 Monmouth Street, W.C.2.

* * *

MODEL RAILWAYS
All kinds of powered systems and all gauge working models of locomotives; reliably-engineered model boats, together with the experience of over 60 years specialisation at BASSETT-LOWKE LTD., 112 High Holborn, London, W.C.1 Showroom and illustrated catalogue.

* * *

CIGARETTE CARDS
A wide range of selected and rare cards from 2/6 to £15 a set, available from I. GOODSTEIN LTD., 16 Charing Cross Road, W.C.2. (TEMple Bar 0631.) Catalogue on request. Mail order service.

* * *

SOUVENIR AND COSTUME DOLLS
THE AUSTRALIAN SOUVENIR SHOP, Surrey Street, Strand, W.C.2, caters for the current vogue for collecting Fashion and Costume-dolls from many lands. Their range includes some very fetching dolls made by Raymond Peynet of France, for example, Napoleon and Josephine, and wistful lovers with a Left Bank look; Maori babies and a koala bear that plays *Waltzing Matilda*, and gay little Australian hobos.

* * *

BOOKS ABOUT DOLLS AND TOYS
An invaluable source for the enthusiast is the delightful secluded bookshop tucked away at 21 Little Russell Street, W.C.1, on the second floor, where a distinguished craftswoman carries on a book service as K. R. DRUMMOND, Bookseller.

Here one may browse over or be advised on, the latest or the out-of-print titles; everything to do with arts and crafts, and a wide range of books on the history of toys, toymaking, dolls, puppetry, model-making, etc. Periodic catalogues are issued on request, wherein often rare books are offered at reasonable prices.

EARLY CHILDREN'S STORYBOOKS

Most of the London and country antiquarian booksellers can offer or obtain to order, popular children's books up to a century or so in age. The bibliophile will find no difficulty in tracking down his best contacts through the trade. As a random list the following names will be found helpful: —

Elkin Mathew Ltd., Takeley, Bishop's Stortford, Herts., who issue a comprehensive Catalogue (List 73) *Early Children's Books*. This firm is under the direction of Mr. Percy Muir, author of *English Children's Books*: 1600-1900, a standard reference work published by B. T. Batsford.

The Times Bookshop, Wigmore Street, W.1. published in 1960 a valuable catalogue *English Children's Books*, 1563-1900, recording an Exhibition held there.

David H. Pratt, 25 Bluebell Road, Bassett, Southampton, Hants., often offers unusual editions.

The Beauchamp Bookshop, 32 Old Brompton Road, S.W.7. is an establishment having long experience in the field, as well as with ephemera, toybooks, paper games and table games, and antique playthings.

The Baldur Bookshop, 44 Hill Rise, Richmond, Surrey. This shop, established in 1933, specialises in Children's Books; ephemera, Scrapbooks and sheets, greeting cards, picture postcards, valentines and prints of juvenile interest; moveable books, panoramic books, novelty and toybooks, juvenile drama, including toy theatre sheets and scenery. Its Proprietor, Mr. Eric Barton is widely known among collectors and the trade, and is always willing to help the genuine enquirer.

Other specialists in the field of early Children's Books are, D. M. Beach of Salisbury; J. D. Miller of Worthing; R. A. Brimmell of Thames Ditton and Messrs. Pickering and Chatto, Orange Street, London. W.C.2.

     *   *   *

The distinguished Ballet and Theatre Critic, Cyril W.

Beaumont, manages the Charing Cross Road bookshop at No. 75, known to balletomanes everywhere. Not all his clientele, however, realise that in his young days he was an enthusiastic and impressionable lover of the Juvenile Theatre —as were so many of that generation. Insight into those days is vividly attained by reading one of Mr. Beaumont's several books privately published at the bookshop address, namely, *Flash-Back* which has a preface by Sacheverell Sitwell.

The editions are strictly limited but the zealot may not leave the shop empty-handed if he tactfully makes it known that he would very much like to own a copy of either *Toy-Rhymes* by Cyril Beaumont, decorations by Eileen Mayo, or *The Wonderful Journey,* (1927) featuring a boy and a rocking-horse; or *The Strange Adventures of a Toy Soldier,* (1926) with decorations by Wyndham Payne—each of them a treasure to the book-lover.

           *   *   *

EDUCATIONAL TOY SPECIALISTS

Today, thanks to advances made in nursery, kindergarten and pre-school education the whole concept of play as a dynamic factor in society has become acceptable to tens of thousands of people as a matter of course. These, because of their training and general outlook, opt for the "useful" and constructional plaything as compared with the conformist and conventional object pre-decided by a nebulous and faceless authority called "the trade".

Thirty years ago this was far from being the case. At that time, quite alone in Britain and attempting to pioneer a new concept of "the right toy for the right age", were Paul and Marjorie Abbatt. The widely-famed toyshop bearing their name, which today stands at 94 Wimpole Street, W.1. is, in one sense, a vivid realisation of the lifework of the Abbatts. It is, of course a unique establishment. Paul and Marjorie Abbatt are purveyors of toys which play a decisive part in the psychological and emotional stimulation and development of children. They have visited all countries to study all children, and for the Abbatts a plaything is not just something pretty or amusing, but really *means* something. For those who cannot conveniently visit the store and see the collection at firsthand, perhaps the best way of getting some idea of what this toyshop represents, and the unique place it occupies in this country, is to write for their current richly-illustrated brochure. This publication reflects in its contents and format some of the inspiration which, down the years, and through the aftermath of War, has brought fulfilment to generations of children—in the playroom, in street and garden and by the sea; in kindergartens and even in hospitals.

The ideology followed by the Abbatt view of play may be summed up in the following excerpts: —

The right toys for children are those which they enjoy the most; toys which they play with over and over again and for long periods. They enjoy such toys because they are in some way or other helpful to them and enable them to do the things they want to.

If parents nowadays attach more importance than formerly to children's play, they are following the trend of expert opinion which holds that the experiences of early childhood, including play, are decisive for personality.

In play, haphazard and trivial as it may appear and apparently containing no element of learning at all, little children are in fact learning lessons that are fundamental to the whole of their education; for instance, the use of language and how to mix with other children, the awareness of their own powers and of themselves as unique individuals, muscular and nervous development and the poise and purpose that come from satisfying activity. They are learning these lessons at their own rhythm and in ways which accord with their ages and natures. From the importance of play follows the importance of toys. Parents now choose toys for their usefulness to children, not for the appeal toys happen to make to them themselves. Toys, it is now understood, are not trivialities, but tools which children need to assist them in their development.

But what sort of toys? How can we choose the toys the child really needs and that suit him at his particular age?

There follows a comprehensive table worked out by age-groups, from eighteen-month-old infants to 8-year-olds, and recommended toys with reasons why desirable.

Another feature of the Abbatt service are their printed Guide Notes on the buying of toys. These are summarised as follows: —

Age:

If parents sometimes make mistakes in toy-buying, it is usually because they choose toys suitable for an older or more mature child. Mentioned in connection with each toy in this catalogue is the earliest age for which it is generally suitable, it may often be given appropriately to a child several years older. This is particularly true of wooden bricks.

Size:

Small children need large toys or toys with large and simple parts. Toys with many small parts are suitable for older children who are sufficiently skilful to handle them.

Colour:

This need not be realistic—an engine can be red, an elephant pink. Colour must be simple and one or two colours are better than many. Toys are often too garish in colour, and in bad taste. A child should have a number of toys in plain wood.

Decoration:

This seldom adds anything of advantage to the child. Whimsical or grotesque decorations often limit the possibilities of a toy for imaginative play.

Safety:

It is most important that a toy be absolutely safe for the age of child who may have access to it. Look out for sharp edges on metal toys; nails or splinters on badly finished wooden toys; eyes which may pull out on soft toys.

Play Possibilities:

Toys must give ample scope for the young child's imagination. Plain bricks are better than those with pictures, because they can represent whatever the child wishes. A simple doll is often loved more than elegant realistic model, because it can take on whatever character the child chooses to give it. Toys that can be put together in many ways are better than those which make fixed designs. An open vehicle, because it can be loaded, has more play possibilities than a closed one.

Durability:

A cheap toy which breaks at first use is the most expensive in the end. Worse, it causes frustration and disappointment. See that wheels and hinges are all fixed; that plastic parts are not too thin; protruding handles strong enough.

Prices:

Judge prices not only in relation to quality of material and workmanship but to the amount of play-value. A toy of high price is not expensive if the child makes much use of it over long periods.

*   *   *

Another important firm which has made a lasting contribution to the development of "toys that teach" is THE EDUCATIONAL SUPPLY ASSOCIATION LTD. (known to teachers as ESA for short), at 233 Shaftesbury Avenue, W.C.2.

Its current catalogue of goods stocked enjoys the title of *The Vital Years* and is the most comprehensive publication in the country catering for the needs of Infant and Junior Schools in respect of play material and apparatus used progressively by the rising generation of trained teachers.

Contents include special sections on Creative and Occupational Play; Basic Skills; Nursery Equipment, etc. This essential reference-book with its 166 pages is a far cry from their first modest catalogue of 1947, and the illustrations are particularly helpful.

Many of the toys have been designed by experts in this

field, such as Nancy Catford and Eric Parkin. These are made specially for the firm in order to ensure that the necessary standards of durability and finish are maintained. Supplementing the exclusive items there is a very wide range of carefully selected proprietary items, including all the popular games, wheeled toys, animal sets, puzzles, constructional and occupational activity toys. Thirty-six pages are devoted to the basic skills of counting, reading and writing. Even elementary science is covered by the Norstedt demonstration sets and the clever but inexpensive Shield Microscope. Music, gardening, road safety and books for younger children published by E.S.A. all find a place in this most comprehensive catalogue, which is available free to schools and institutions.

E.S.A. have for long recognised that not only the schools but members of the public want to be able to buy sound "Toys that teach". Their shop at the New Oxford Street end of Shaftesbury Avenue caters for the parent who cares about these things, besides carrying one of the largest stocks of children's books in London.

*   *   *

The newest shop for Educational Toys in London is that of JAMES GALT & Co., LTD., 30/31 Great Marlborough Street, W.1. They have a spacious and well-laid-out showroom (to the rear of Liberty & Co.), where parents and teachers may browse and examine what is new. The company has been associated with schools for a hundred and thirty years, first through printing stationery and supplying school text-books, later through play materials and apparatus for the school-room, and during the past two years, catering for the general public through a wide range of constructional and pedagogic toys.

The company's aim is to foster and encourage the demand for good toys from a much wider section of the public than has been done up to now; they believe that young mothers of the next few years will want for their children the same sort of toys as they themselves enjoyed in infant and nursery school.

In their factory at Cheadle, Cheshire, the company specialises in the production of large wooden toys and other school equipment, large trucks and wagons, wooden engines and prams and climbing apparatus, large blocks and bricks and play-furniture. A modern silkscreen department produces wooden jig-saws as well as a very wide range of teaching aids.

They publish a comprehensive catalogue and, like the firms above-mentioned, have an expanding Mail Order service.

OUTSIDE LONDON

MARIONETTES AND WOODEN DOLLS

One of the leading authorities in this field is WALDO LANCHESTER, creator of the Marionette Theatre named after him. His shop and workshop at 39 Henley Street, Stratford-on-Avon, Warwickshire, is a kind of Mecca for the puppeteer and the lay enthusiast.

Everything to do with Marionettes and the Toy Theatre is known to him and his wife, as they have worked all over Britain and are devoted to their craft. Situated in the Shakespearean town his charming shop carries a stock of tasteful objects of interest to theatre-lovers, young and old alike. Advice and help to students of the Puppet Theatre and the Juvenile Drama are freely given. Mr. Lanchester has made a study of wooden dolls (the inarticulated precursors of our wooden marionettes), which we in England have learned to call "Dutch" dolls, and he has published a monograph about them.

Another of his "finds" were a number of traditional old wooden horses from Bolzano, Italy, which are in mint condition and of great interest to toy collectors.

His excellent range of books about puppets is of vast help to the student; *Dutch Doll to Marionette,* a miniature folded data-sheet contains diagrams and instructions for making a proper marionette out of one of these.

*　　　*　　　*

THE DOLLS' HOUSE, 84 High Street, Broadway, Worcestershire, run by Mrs. Joan Cope (*see also page* 105) specialises in dolls old and new.

Dolls' house furniture, cradles, rush seated chairs, and doll accessories in the way of clothes, handbags, hats, nylons, bracelets and necklets, even school bags and geometry sets.

Toys are mostly of wood, many being the old traditional design in modern guise, such as nested dolls, pecking hens and miniature horses and carts.

Books about dolls, dollmaking and toymaking. Models to cut out and make up and Pop-up books.

A large variety of Corn Dollies are usually on show. These come from counties in England where the traditional designs are still being made. From Denmark come the Straw Mobiles, with tiny straw dolls to sway in the slightest breeze.

Pottery models of *Winnie the Pooh* and *Alice in Wonderland* characters, together with tops and whips, marbles and miniature roundabouts, all add gaiety to a shop window in this most famous of the Cotswold historic villages.

*   *   *

BRIGHTON and its famous Lanes, choc-a-bloc with curio and antique shops is a happy hunting ground for the doll and toy enthusiast. Many dealers draw from sources not available to their London counterparts and will keep for the serious collector special items once a relationship is set up.

Besides the Lanes, however, there is a network of small streets in the vicinity of the Royal Pavilion, and here, at No. 9 Bond Street (Brighton 25516) is an unassuming shop known as Françoise of Paris.

Owned by an Englishman and his French wife, this place is a "must" for the seeker after miscellaneous Victoriana. One may be shown Dolls' Houses and furniture, games, books, rocking-horses, and so on, but the principal attraction for the serious enthusiast is a room containing the stock of some two or three hundred playdolls, mostly late Victorian or Edwardian. Madame Françoise travels regularly to France, and may be relied on to keep a sharp look-out for a customer's particular needs.

THE DOLL'S HOUSE, Ditchling Road, Brighton; specialises in modern dolls and accessories. Owned by Mr. and Mrs. Render, it offers a Doll Hospital Service.

Mr. Render does most of the repairing and his wife makes the dollies' outfits. "I only use the best," she said, "I love these dolls and should hate to use cheap material."

There are tie-up shoes, button-up, high-heeled shoes and high-heeled sandals for the teenage dolls, also Sheridan shoes with a huge buckle in front.

Socks can be tiny ankle-length in cotton interlock, knee-length knitted silk, or full-length seamed nylon.

The slips are paper nylon petticoats that stick out, with nylon, lace-trimmed panties to match. The bedwear fashion seems to be shorties, or pyjamas in candy-striped cotton, and pretty Winceyette for colder nights.

Dresses can be drip-dry cotton to a grosgrain party dress, nylon or taffeta; also evening dresses and brocade wedding gowns, all exquisitely hand-made to fit your doll if you wish.

For cold days there are velour coats with fur collars, muffs and bonnets to match. And, of course, plastic macs, with hoods attached, or rubberised coats with sou'westers and real rubber wellington boots.

The little accessories are too many for me to mention, but do look at the Italian straw hats and the tiny satchels filled with an exercise book and six-sided pencil.

A reliable source in the Oxfordshire region is: ROGER WARNER, of Burford (Burford 2114).

MODEL AND TOY VEHICLES

An interesting stock is usually held by W. F. Greenwood & Sons, Ltd., antique dealers, 3 Crown Place, Harrogate, Yorks.

PART VIII

HAND-CRAFTED TOYS AND THEIR MAKERS
BRITISH TOYMAKERS' GUILD

Enquiries to the Honorary Secretary, Mrs. D. Masterson,
107 Calbourne Road, London, S.W.12.

The British Toymakers' Guild was formed in 1956 by a handful of craftsmen and craftswomen who deplored the increasing manufacture of shoddy, mass produced toys which were flooding the markets. It was felt that some active steps should be taken to encourage and foster the making of hand-made toys.

The Guild, which does not undertake to sell toys, does, by means of exhibitions, help members to bring their wares to the notice of the public and to the buyers of the big stores. The Guild also helps members by suggesting ways of marketing their goods.

Some members are full-time toy makers, others produce toys as a lucrative part-time pleasure, but all of them aim at a high quality and of course all designs are original.

Every member of the Guild is a high-class toymaker, though for some toymaking is only a hobby. Others, however, are professional designers and their work will be on sale this Christmas at many of the most exclusive stores. But they influence the character and design of toys not only by direct sales of this kind, but by making models for window display purposes, for museums and exhibitions, and for private collectors.

But the Guild does not limit its membership only to successfully established toymakers. Even the amateur who really shares this enthusiasm can apply for admission, if she is prepared to submit specimens of her work. These are considered by the Guild committee which meets monthly, and if the standard of workmanship and design is high enough admission will be granted.

The subscription for membership is £1 1s. yearly, and members can attend lectures, exhibitions, puppet-shows, film shows and demonstrations on toymaking, all designed to help them improve and enlarge the range of their work. Toy enthusiasts, who do not aspire to be actual makers, can become associate members for a fee of 10/6 yearly, and have the right also to attend these functions.

Sam Smith, The Golf House, Kingswear, Dartmouth, Devon, is an accomplished craftsman in wood, artist, illustrator and journalist. Among his many activities before World War II he made some toys which in his own words "while being English in conception were in a style unique in this country's toy production. So much so that one retailer then told me of a customer who had refused to believe they were British-made!"

His gaily-painted toy boats, canal-barges, yachts and dinghies are as English as the Devonian waters near his home. They combine an original design with just that tinge of Heath-Robinsonian levity and Lewis Carrol fantasy which add up to superb toymanship. Indeed the "Sam Smith Toyman" on his earlier notepaper was a title aptly given, for many of these early "down to the sea in ships" series are now collectors' pieces.

That sparkle and love of a joke have developed in his work since, with a group of helpers just after the war, Sam Smith started a small factory. His hope was to use machines and rationalised production methods and yet retain qualities of personality and individuality in everything attempted. For two years they succeeded, but the advent of a heavy purchase tax made his toys inaccessible to the middle public. So he returned to drawing, "and as a second string to newspaper cartooning".

Of later years, this love of a joke has imbued his occasional toymaking with a surrealist quality. And, oddly enough, where Sam Smith Toyman was prevented from reaching a mass public, Sam Smith Sophisticate is much in demand as the principal creator of Toys For Grown-ups in Britain today. His objects are all highly individual works, brilliantly conceived and executed, with a fine feeling for wood—his favourite medium. In the fashionable studios of Mayfair and Chelsea no "with-it" decor is complete without one of his crazy, or just funny-haha, playthings, particularly those ridiculous Jumping Jacks and other "fantasies-of-movement".

He is one of the few artist-craftsmen who has been accorded one-man exhibitions as painters are in West End galleries and studios. Most of these are held at PRIMAVERA, 149 Sloane Street, S.W.1, for whom he exclusively supplies work, under such fetching titles as *Coastal Waters* (featuring his early love for boats), or *Microcosm*, a collection of humorous or very satirical toy-things.

These shows are memorable occasions in that most of the mechanical designs and zany gadgetry are snapped up during the previews of Smith fans! He also designs his own Invitation Cards and devises titles for the catalogue, e.g.: —

> I Saw Three Cows
>
> Guiders Angela and Grace Goodsworthy
>
> Punting Lovers
>
> Seaside Flag Salesman
>
> The Busts
>
> Espresso Japano
>
> Group of Angels.

Yootha Rose

In the first rank of British toymaker-artists this remarkable woman is interested in toys at all levels—creatively, since the designs and makes a wide range of original objects, some of them masterpieces in miniature; historically, since she is a Trustee of The Toy Museum, Rottingdean, and a co-founder of the Pollock Toy Theatre collection; theatrically, since her training as a stage designer with Nigel Playfair has given her a flair for mounting toy exhibitions; and "evangelically", since she is an active member of the British Toymakers' Guild, the aims of which are set forth on page 220.

Miss Lesley Gordon, author of *Peepshow Into Paradise* (Harrap), herself a toymaker, toy historian, writer and illustrator, has described her meeting with Yootha Rose thus:—

A model caravan, perfect in every detail, stood at the end of the passage, and in the window a chandelier of wooden angels, reminiscent of the charming "Weihnachtsengels" of pre-war Germany, revolved gently in the breeze.

Yootha Rose is one of the few toy craftsmen, or even rarer, craftswomen, left to us, and as such it is good to know that her work is appreciated all over the world. Carve and paint as hard as she may, and the multitude of merry-go-rounds, swing-boats, coster carts, and toy villages, that surrounded us bore silent witness to the fact, Yootha Rose can never "catch up" with her orders.

At an exhibition a year or two ago, 20,000 orders came in in three days for these gay and vital little toys. Queen Mary, with her delight in tiny things of good craftsmanship, became an early patron, and now the dancing and circus figures are giving pleasure to Princess Anne and Prince Charles. A documentary film has been made of her and her methods of work.

Yootha Rose is one of those fortunate artists with a foot in both worlds; the world of children and the world of grown-ups. To young and old, parent or collector, her work makes an instant appeal. It is simple and durable enough for the nursery, and yet so cunningly contrived, no figures ever exactly repeated, that having made a purchase with a small nephew or niece in view, one has to be really self-sacrificing to give it up!

Yootha Rose received her early training at the Lyric Theatre, Hammersmith, where she designed costumes and sets for Nigel Playfair's productions, but it was not until the second world war that her interest in toy-making was aroused. Like many another craftsmen, she found that these dark days of evacuation and air-raid shelters brought some recompense, for it was while staying in a Dorset village that Yootha first started making toys for her own small daughter and for the village children.

When there were no toys to buy in the shops, Yootha Rose made toys enough to decorate the village Christmas tree, and thus it was among these stern small critics that she served her apprenticeship.

Her equipment is simple—a bench crowded with pieces of wood, wire, and glue, a selection of knives and brushes, and innumerable pots of paint. Her motto is simple, too—"Toys should not only be beautiful to look at, but should *do* something." Her name, Yootha, is Australian aboriginal. It means "Bringer of Good", and she has indeed brought good to an immense number of children.

Nancy Catford, 43 Churston Gardens, Bounds Green, N11, was for many years on the panel of toy designers and makers for the Educational Supply Association and who specialised in kindergarten and Nursery School "Do It Yourself" playthings from discarded objects during the years of wartime austerity. In this field she won a reputation for originality and industry and helped many teachers solve play problems. She is also a potter and modeller and, having made a significant contribution to toy-design in Britain, she has returned to her other crafts.

Being skilled in using tools, Nancy Catford's books (for she numbers authorship among her accomplishments) have chapters on the use thereof, which are appreciated by parents and teachers alike. Her excellent handbook, *Making Your Own Party Decorations* has a chapter also about how to make those playthings from "Nature's harvest", as our Victorian ancestors were so fond of doing. Birds and hedgehogs from teasels; Easter eggs and tortoises from walnut shells; storks and owls from fir cones; snakes from acorn cups; and animal tails, beards and ruffs from fur and feathers. Everything from sea-shells to bottle-tops!

There are few possibilities for making amusing toys from household things that she has not profitably explored, e.g., corks and clothespegs; coloured spills and pipe-cleaners; paper doilies and crepe-paper; cotton-wool, cotton reels, silver paper—scores of fascinating novelties and decorations for party or Christmas tree are all carefully detailed in this practical and imaginative book.

Winsome Douglass is one of a group of talented young needlewomen who have come from West Hartlepool, where she teaches Art at Dyke House Secondary Modern School for Girls, and has also taught for five years at the local College of Art. Her speciality is the design and execution of fine embroidery, and also soft toys, and her books *Discovering Embroidery* (1955) and *Toys for Your Delight* (1957), both published by Messrs. Mills & Boon Ltd., adequately demonstrate her skill and fertility of invention in these fields.

Anne Scott

At Melrose in the Scottish Border country an ancient craft has been given a new twist; the traditional materials of the long famous Italian and German doll-makers have been replaced by picture wire, barbola and the products of modern factories; these are fashioned into dolls perfect in proportion and correct in every detail of dress. Each represents a Scottish celebrity, even to facial likeness where possible. Each is a collector's piece, but to Mrs. Anne Scott their construction is no more than just a fascinating hobby, worked at between running a home and looking after her three children.

Mrs. Scott has been making since she was twelve years old.

In the series she has produced in the last three years most represent personalities from the Scottish history books. Heads and faces are modelled in barbola, the features and even the expression copies where possible from contemporary portraits in the Scottish National Portrait Gallery. Beards and hair fashioned from alpaca and sheep's wool are added where appropriate. The skeleton of wire and wool is finally dressed in hand-sewn clothes which follow in every detail the fashion of the period—the chain mail of Wallace and Bruce, the beribboned mandolin of David Rizzo, Jenny Geddes' striped petticoat. Each is the outcome of much research and many hours of delicate work by nimble fingers.

All sorts of material is grist to her mill. Panels of "embroidery" on Queen Margaret's gown turn out to be scraps of old Paisley shawl. Wallace and Bruce must needs have mail armour, and a chain purse that someone contributed is useful here. John Knox is in minatory mood, but there is a real touch of faery about Thomas the Rhymer, the Queen and her steed of tulle.

Colin Woods conducts what he describes as the third big gest industry in Llanarmon. He concedes first and second place to agriculture and quarrying.

His industry—making toys and souvenirs for tourists—is small but thriving.

Mr. Woods often works until the early hours of the morning to cope with the orders that pour into his white-washed workshop from all parts of the country.

Crowded with wooden farms, castles and all sorts of souvenirs, the workshop is a children's paradise. For Mr. Woods, at least, there is no worry about what to get the children for Christmas.

Mr. Woods and his wife have registered themselves as Cave Toys, a name they derive from a natural cave situated opposite their house. They have the official backing of the Welsh Rural Industries Bureau, and as far as they know they are the only people in North Wales engaged on this sort of work.

They had a stand recently at the Welsh rural crafts exhibition at Llandudno and have frequently exhibited at Llangollen International Eisteddfod and agricultural shows.

Barbara J. Barlow (Mrs.), Hobbicrafts (Knightsbridge) Ltd., 3 Trevor Street London, S.W.7. Tel.: Kensington 3809.
Author-Designer of the "Hobbie" Toy Knitting Book and "More Hobbie Knitted Toys", 5/- each.
Soft, cuddly knitted animals, suitable for children of all ages. Sales in limited numbers to shops. Personal orders may be sent direct. List and prices on request.

Charles Bolton, 23 Manor Drive, Whetstone, London, N.20. Tel.: Enterprise 3147.
Model furniture. Designed and made to scale, these handcrafted miniatures are modelled on English period pieces. Orders should be placed direct.

Helena H. Clarke (Mrs.), Aldham House, Ryton-on-Tyne, Co. Durham. Tel.: Ryton 2188.
Animal families, e.g., rabbits, bears, with soft bodies; handmade clothes.

Maud Cranfield, A.R.C.A. (Miss), 40 Leopold Road, Wimbledon, London, S.W.19. Tel.: Wimbledon 3557.
Soft toys of unusual design suitable for children of all ages. Exhibition pieces made to order. Toys may be obtained from Messrs. Harrods, Heals, Libertys and Stonehenge Woollen Ind. Ltd. of London.

Faith Eaton (Miss), 16 Clifton Gardens, London, W.9. Tel.: Cunningham 4240.
Designs three types of dolls in addition to special orders: (1) Play dolls; wooden heads, soft bodies costumed as English characters. (2) Collectors' models; authentically, costumed as English characters, "London Cries", etc. (3) Minia-

227

ture wooden dolls, from $\frac{1}{4}''$ to $1''$ mainly, costumed as required.

Orders should be placed direct. Detailed price list on application.

P. Grace Furse (Mrs.), 5 *Wilmington Square, W.C.*1. *Tel.*: *Terminus* 0489.

Soft Toys. Hand embroidered felt animals—attractive colour—contemporary design. Orders should be placed direct.

*John Gould, 1 Montbelle Road, London S.E.*9.

Wooden toys of modern design. Small representations of various vehicles, strongly constructed of hardwood; brightly coloured and finished in durable synthetic lacquer. Toys may be purchased at Heals or orders placed direct.

Clifford Heap, 219 High Road, Buckurst Hill, Essex. Tel.: *Buckurst Hill* 2044.

Miniature theatre. Each production lasts for one hour and can be played to audiences up to 150. Productions include Cinderella, Aladdin, Beauty and the Beast, etc. etc. All enquiries made direct to Mr. Heap.

Margaret Hutchings (Mrs.), *The Manor House, Ongar, Essex. Tel.*: *Ongar* 2633.

Designer and maker of toys, dolls, decorations and "display pieces". Models not usually for sale. Author of "Glove Toys" (Studio Ltd.), "Modern Soft Toys", "Dolls and How to Make Them" (Mills and Boon). Writer and designer for the press. T.V. Demonstrator.

Gwynne Madge (Mrs.), *"Yondover", Birtley Green, Bramley, Surrey. Tel.*: *Bramley* 2580.

Soft Toys. Speciality "Tildabear", white teddy, fully dressed, hand smocked dress. "Loretta", mascot lamb. "Mousey", small white or grey mouse. All Nylon Fabric, foam filled and washable. Limited orders should be placed direct.

John Spence, Elmfield School, Love Lane, Stourbridge, Worcs.
Wooden toys aimed to stimulate the imagination of the
growing child through movement and colour. Designs
range from simple animal cut-outs to such moving toys as
wood-choppers and washerwomen—hand-carved and indivi-
dually coloured. Also rocking boats and nursery furniture.
Orders should be placed direct.

I. Spencer Smith (Mrs.), 19 Queen's Gate Place, London,
S.W.7.
Dressed, miniature character dolls; wire and pin construc-
tion. Not for sale.

Peggy Tearle (Miss), 202 London Road, Leicester. Tel.:
Leicester 4419.
Designer and maker of soft toys, animal models and col-
lectors' dolls. Author of "Circus Toys", "Felt Glove Pup-
pets" and "Felt Dolls to Make and Dress" (Dryad Press).
Writer on craft subjects for the Press. Speaker and demon-
strator on craft subjects.
Sales in limited numbers to shops or to special order.
Animal models sold through Crafts Centre of Great Britain.

Beryl Waugh (Mrs.), De Montalt Lodge, Summer Lane,
Combe Down, Bath Som.
Soft dolls, made in various velvets, dressed in nylon,
brocade, etc., stuffed pure kapok. Character toys with long
arms and legs from 14-30" in height. Orders should be
placed direct.

Doreen Masterson (Mrs.), 107 Calbourne Road, London,
S.W.12.
Decorative Dinosaurs and other animals made of stuffed
felt, embroidered with coloured metallic and other threads.
Orders should be placed direct.
Colourful soft felt toys, e.g., balls, clowns, etc. Also nursery

cushions. Obtainable Harrods, Heals, Otway Toy Studio, or orders may be placed direct.

Alan Quincey, A.T.D., 192 Havering Road, Romford, Essex.
Wooden toys. Sturdy, brightly-coloured, whimsical vehicles having a period flavour, with removable peg-doll passengers and drivers. Western train, two-seat car, taxi, steamroller, etc. Enquiries and orders should be made direct.

D. C. Reid (Mrs.), 108 Castelnau, London, S.W.13. Tel.: Riverside 3716.
Soft cuddly animals made of nylon fabric. Rabbits obtainable from Stonehenge Woollen Ind. Ltd. Orders should be placed direct for Teddy Bears and other animals.

Yootha Rose (Miss), 24 Clermont Terrace, Brighton 6.
Carved and painted wooden dolls and toys. Caravans, Dolls' houses, Noah's Ark, etc., also composition and cloth dolls, including dolls with china heads, arms and legs. Exhibition organiser. Exhibitions so far arranged include: "Children's Paradise", "Model Soldiers", Pollocks Toy Theatre and Toy Museum, "Dolls—Toys and Theatres", "The Toy Museum Collection". Orders and enquiries should be made direct.

M. E. Rowlatt (Mrs.), 14 Addison Road, Kensington, London, W.14. Tel.: Park 5246.
Soft toys of felt and fur fabric.

Denise Williams, A.R.Cam.A. (Mrs. D. M. Hinckley) 90 Elsham Road, London W.14. Tel.: Park 3757.
Designer and maker of angels, wise men, madonnas and decorations. Each item original and unique. (Not for rough handling.) Sales to shops. Enquiries and orders should be made direct.

Susan Wynter, Toy Trumpet Workshops, 31 Onslow Gardens, London, N.10. Tel.: TUD 5232.

Maker of original working wooden toys. Nursery Tableaux and Nativity sets. Enquiries direct.

Hermione L. F. Cubitt, Greystone, Rodborough Common, near Stroud, Glos.,

Specialises in needlework figures and character dolls—even the faces are worked on silk. The historical characters include English Kings and Queens; the figure of King Charles II is surrounded by members of his Court. This craftswoman lectures and demonstrates at centres arranged by the Gloucestershire Women's Institute.

Dorothy Dumas, "Woodpeckers", Snakey Lane, Preston Park, Brighton, Sussex.

Makes fine dolls and exquisite dolls' furniture to scale. The miniature items vary from 1" to 1' high and the period covered is 1450 to 1850. Limited orders are accepted from collectors.

Roma Ferguson c/o the Dollmakers' Circle.

Creates character dolls made of wire and wadding covered with silk. Samples of her figures include George IV ('Prinny'), Charles II, in perfect period dress, and contrasting pairs of Pierrots.

Olga Sieves, 129 Beaufort Street, Chelsea, S.W.1.

Specialises in Topsey Turvey Dolls of which there are few makers today. Her dolls are all very gaily coloured and include dual-faced themes such as Red Ridinghood and

Wolf; The Inn-keeper's Daughter; and Dick Turpin with and without disguise. Write for appointment.

Elizabeth D. Williams, West Worthing, Sussex.

Makes needlework Portrait Dolls Article in her "Queens of England" in *Housewife Magazine* (Coronation edition): Exhibits regularly at Arundel Castle, Sussex in aid of Charity. Her *Mary Queen of Scots* has been acquired by Museum of Childhood, Edinburgh.

Violet Potter.

Makes unique dolls for Peter Jones Ltd. Embroidered faces, long limbs, undressing cloths, from modern "child" dolls to "Madonnas". Exhibition at Foyle's Gallery: *Dolls With a Difference*.

G. E. Russell, c/o Dollmakers' Circle.

Specialises in Rag Dolls and a range of fetching Nursery Rhyme dolls. Lives in Devon.

Beatrice Belcher c/o Dollmakers' Circle.

Makes models of famous characters ancient and contemporary. Lives in Dorset.

Eric and Joy Parkin, Brook House, The Green, Harlow, Essex.

Design and make educational toys of all kinds. Their work is valued by the E.S.A. for which they have supplied new variants over the years for jigsaw-puzzles, alphabet games, telling-the-time devices, and constructional toys having a contemporary trend.

PLATE XLI

More Toys by Yootha Rose. (See pp. 223-224)

Plate XLII

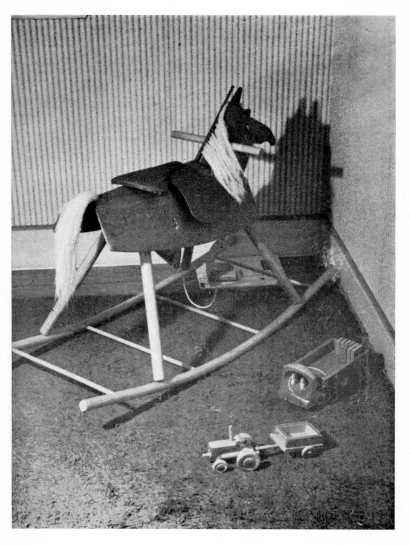

Rocking Horse & Wheeled Toys by John Gould. (See p. 228)

PLATE XLIII

Period Dolls' Furniture by Charles Bolton. (See p. 227)

PLATE XLIV

Designs by Ursula Blau

PLATE XLV

Gordon Hand's Antique Shop. (See pp. 184-185)

PLATE XLVI

Embroidered Models of British Queens by Lilian Lunn. (See p. 107)

PLATE XLVII

Italian Dolls on Show at the Italian Institute for Foreign Trade. (See p. 203)

PLATE XLVIII

"Sunday Pictorial" National Exhibition of Children's Art. (See pp. 251-253)

PLATE XLIX

"A Toy for a Sick Child" Fund. (See pp. 242-245)

PART IX

MISCELLANEOUS INFORMATION

MATERIALS FOR TOY-MAKING

These can be obtained through most handicraft shops catering for schools and home hobbies. Every British city, and the majority of towns, has at least one such supplier and the local Chamber of Commerce will provide details if written to.

London is no exception, being well-provided centrally and in the suburbs.

One of the best-known sources of supply is the Dryad Showrooms, situated at 93 Great Russell Street, W.C.1. (Tel: MUS 0234), near the British Museum. Here the visitor is invited to inspect stocks and browse among a comprehensive range of materials, tools and equipment for more that fifty crafts.

Among the latter toy-making features prominently in the Dryad service. Advice is given to parents and beginners; to teachers and enthusiastic homecraft hobby-ists. Materials include: raffia and cane; papers, cardboard and similar compositions; fabrics ranging from felt to woven cloths and flock; wood of all kinds; straw; leather; plastic; cord; and other materials used for embroidering and finishing.

Descriptive leaflets and an up-to-date booklet are available on request. The latter is issued by the Dryad Publishing House in Leicester, part of the firm's organisation, which has specialised in books on toy and model-making. This business was first established after World War I to supply materials for educational and occupational therapy handicrafts. It has now expanded and numbers among its writers and authorities on toy-making such leading crafts-people as Peggy Tearle, Waldo S. Lanchester and Winifred Horton.

The following practical books are among current Dryad publications and the shilling Leaflet Series on Toy-making may be thoroughly recommended.

SOFT TOY MAKING AND FELT WORK

MORE SOFT TOYS by Joy Ogden and Mary Wilcox

Instructions and full-sized patterns for making a number of realistic animals and birds in fur baize, including lion cub, kitten, panda, penguin and three dogs. They are all most attractive toys, which will give much satisfaction in the making to the craft worker, and which any small child would love to possess.

5th edition. 36 pp. and full-sized patterns. Illustrated. Net 5s.

CUT WOOLLY TOYS by Mochrie and I. P. Roseaman

These charming toys are simply made by wrapping coloured wools on cardboard foundations, which are afterwards removed and the wool clipped to shape. They are most life-like and attractive, yet so soft and cuddly that they are ideal for the nursery.

6th edition. 36 pp. Illustrated. Net 3s. 6d.

RAG BAG TOYS

Here are eleven professional-looking toys from the sort of oddments every housewife accumulates—a giraffe from a scrap of gingham, a cheerful darkie doll from an old felt hat,

'Simple Simon' from worn-out wool stockinette undies, a golliwog from an old black swim-suit. All the toys are simple to make.

14th edition. 48 pp. Full-sized patterns. Illustrated. Net 3s. 6d.

FELT DOLLS TO MAKE AND DRESS by Peggy Tearle

These toys of charm and character are designed for simplicity in making. Dolls and clothes are cut from felt squares with the minimum of patterns, and can easily be attempted by young children. The dolls represent children in various indoor and outdoor clothes for playtime activities, together with their poodle and a pony, and the clothes are attractive and easily changed.

2nd edition. 58 pp. including plates. Illustrated. Net 5s.

CIRCUS TOYS by Peggy Tearle

The author, who has demonstrated toy-making on television, and is a member of the Crafts Centre and the Arts and Crafts Exhibition Society, has captured the atmosphere of the circus ring in these twelve enchanting figures and animals. They include a Ringmaster, Clown, Ballerina, horses, bears, a performing seal, and a charming little Toby Dog, all in traditional costume and trappings.

3rd edition. 60 pp. and full-sized patterns. Illustrated. Net 6s.

FELT TOYS by E. Mochrie and I. P. Roseaman

These twelve lively toys include terrier, elephant, monkey, rabbit and horse. Easy to make with the aid of the full-sized patterns, they provide great satisfaction both for craft worker and recipient. They can also be made in leather or leather cloth.

17th edition. 41 pp. and full-sized patterns. Illustrated. Net 5s.

DRESSED SOFT TOYS—ANIMAL FAMILIES
by Edith Moody

Families of toys always have a tremendous appeal, and this delightfully illustrated book provides all the instructions for making and dressing Wally Bear, Fred Fox, Percy Pig, Mick Monkey, William Rabbit, their wives and babies.

4th edition. 32 pp. and full-sized patterns. Illustrated. Net 4s.

WOODEN TOY MAKING by Winifred Horton

A really creative approach to toy-making. Instead of working from measured drawings, the teacher is encouraged to suggest forms and construction, which will enable the pupil to carry out his own ideas with the maximum of enjoyment. Toys from waste wood, toys with simple movement (monkey on a stick, wrestlers, etc.), wheeled toys (bird with flapping wings) are described and illustrated, together with notes on equipment and making.

6th edition. 56 pp. Illustrated in colour. Cloth boards.

Net 8s. 6d.

PUPPETRY

HAND PUPPETS AND STRING PUPPETS
by Waldo S. Lanchester, F.R.S.A.

Those who have seen the Lanchester Marionette Theatre will know that, as a professional puppet showman, Waldo Lanchester is both artist and craftsman. This edition of his book is completely revised and considerably enlarged. It describes the making, dressing and operating of both glove and string puppets of every type and the construction of puppet theatres, while animal puppets are dealt with in a new illustrated chapter.

10th edition. 56 pp. and charts. Profusely illustrated.

Net 7s. 6d.

ANIMAL GLOVE PUPPETS

Describes the making of a range of glove puppets which will stimulate the imagination of children and grown-ups alike. Instructions and diagrams are clear and straightforward and the photographs of Teddy, Fox, Badger, Panda, Cat and Owl provide suggestions for a delightful puppet play.

18 pages. Illustrated. Net 2s. 6d.

THE SHILLING-LEAFLET SERIES

SIX WOOLLY DOLLS
These appealing dolls are made on the principle of the cut woolly ball, and include Schoolgirl, Man Friday, Clown, Jester, Columbine and Pierrot.
16 pages. Illustrated. Leaflet No. 156

DOLL MAKING WITH THE PROFESSIONAL TOUCH
Instructions and diagrams for making and dressing different types of dolls. 12 pages. Illustrated. Leaflet No. 123

MAKING WOOLLY TOYS
Instructions and diagrams for making small animals and toys with woolly twist.
12 pages. Illlustrated. Leaflet No. 113

SMALL CARVED ANIMALS by F. Haslam
Instructions for carving simple animals, including mouse, polar bear, piglet, and giraffe.
12 pages. Illustrated. Leaflet No. 133

CARVED AND JOINTED ANIMALS by F. Haslam
Instructions for built-up and jointed animals, including pig, horse, rabbit and elephant.
12 pages. Illustrated. Leaflet No. 134

RAFFIA FIGURES AND ANIMALS
In this new Leaflet, the Dutch Girl and Flamingo are brought together with other favourite toys including the Huntsman, Horse and Hounds, Red Indian on Horseback, Dog, Owl, Duck, Pig and Dragonfly.
12 pages. Illustrated. Leaflet No. 161

PUNCH AND JUDY PUPPETS by Peggy Tearle
Revised and enlarged to include full instructions and patterns for making Dog Toby as well as Punch, Judy, Policeman and Sambo.
16 pages. Illustrated. Leaflet No. 148

237

WOOD IN TOYMAKING

Mr. N. M. Gibson, "Coedfa", Llanbedr, Ruthin, Denbighshire, has chosen this subject for an original research thesis.

In this he outlines historically how wooden toys developed from the Early Egyptian examples now in museums, to their modern counterparts made at the present time. He identifies the types of timber used and attempts to give reasons for their usage.

He is concerned primarily with values of good workmanship and with British-made toys as contrasted with foreign ones. He has made a special study of workmanship as practised by the craft-carpenter apprentices and of the fine pieces they had to make as model furniture. The end-products of so many of these exercises became Doll's House furniture and children's playthings and Mr. Gibson relates this aspect to the use of, and need for, wood in toy-making.

PERIODICAL

A recommended magazine dealing with aspects of toy-making among the other crafts is: *Crafts Review*, Edited by Murray Fieldhouse, Pendley Manor, Tring, Herts. (Annual subscription, £1.)

DOLLS' HOSPITALS

Most established Toy Shops (see pages 179 *et seq*) are in touch with repair units and factory managements who can supply a run-of-the-mill service for breakages.

Delicate workmanship, however, is not so easy to secure, and most of the Doll's Hospitals, once familiar in certain London districts, have closed down.

Readers are referred to the list of doll-makers in other sections of this Guide (pages 95 and 220) among whom the majority will accept repair work if written to first.

Miss Hickman's Doll Shop, 15 Moscow Road, Queensway, London, W.2., (Tel.: Park 7880) undertakes repair of period and antique dolls, and will replace broken features e.g. glass eyes, new hair, etc.

Miss Yootha Rose (see Page 223) restored antique toys for the Toy Museum at Rottingdean and will accept a limited amount of commissions.

Mr. S. F. Sunley (see Page 168) will undertake to repair every mechanical toys. He will refer enquirers wishing to have type of automaton, musical-box movement and similar fabric costumes made or repaired to competent needlewomen with experience of this work. Mrs. Butler, 91 Portobello Road, W.11., can also recommend seamstresses for this job.

Miss Faith Eaton, 16 Clifton Gardens, W.9., restores wax dolls as a speciality. From many collections dolls have reached her in fragments, minus hair, eyes, fingers etc. With matching wax every effort is taken to build up lost parts. Limbs also supplied for old composition and porcelain dolls, Estimates free.

ORGANISATIONS AND INSTITUTIONS CONCERNED WITH CHILD WELFARE OR CHILDREN'S PLAY

Advisory Centre for Education: 14 Buckingham Street, London, W.C.2. Provide information and answer questions about child education at all levels.

Council for Children's Welfare: 54 Platt's Lane, N.W.3. Is concerned with research regarding children's welfare, such as comics, television, play and education.

Council for Children's Play Activities, 94 Wimpole Street, W.1., is composed of experts in all fields relating to the play life of the child in the modern world. Issues reports, research documents, organises exhibitions and holds a conference from time to time in the U.K. or on the Continent.

Embroiderers' Guild, 73 Wimpole Street, W.1. Membership open to all interested in embroidery. Information bureau including data on embroidered soft toys; books on loan, evening classes.

National Froebel Foundation, 2 Manchester Square, London. W.1. Concerned with education of children up to 12 years of age and in the training and examination of kindergarten teachers. Membership opened to all interested; summer schools, lecture courses, library, publications.

Montessori International Training Course: 1 Park Crescent, London. W.1. For all interested in education and child psychology. Books and apparatus available to members of the Montessori Society, at same address.

National Book League, 7 Albemarle Street, W.1. Advisory service includes children's books of all kinds suitable for specific age-groups; holds book exhibitions on its premises, and for hire.

The British Toy-makers' Guild exists to make and market members' handcrafted toys. Hon. Secretary's address: Mrs. D. Masterson, 107 Calbourne Road, London, S.W.12. (See Page 220 for fuller information.)

Nursery School Association of Great Britain and Northern Ireland, 89 Stamford Street, London. S.E.1., supplies information about running nursery schools, teacher training, provides or publishes literature on all aspects of child care; arranges lectures and courses on young children.

Royal School of Needlework, 25 Princess Gate, London. S.W.7., is a training school for teachers and others. Private lessons are available in stitchery. Specialist work in embroidered soft toys.

Pre-School Playgroups Association, 4a Cavendish Mews South, London. W.1., exists to help parents to provide safe and satisfying play for pre-school children (3-5 year olds). Its aims include the stimulation of general interest in nursery education; to encourage parent-education through lectures and discussion groups, leading to a better understanding of the needs of the pre-school child. Groups run their own nursery play programmes. An annual conference is held.

The Save The Children Fund, 12 Upper Belgrave Street, London. S.W.1. This Fund cares for all children everywhere regardless of race or creed.

New Education Fellowship has its international office at 1 Park Crescent, London. W.1. Its magazine, *The New Era*, is published monthly.

FOR FURTHER READING

Design for Play, Lady Allen of Hurtwood F.I.L.A.

Play Parks for Housing New Towns & Parks, Lady Allen of Hurtwood F.I.L.A.

Play with a Purpose, Ministry of Health.

Some Play Materials for Children under Eight, Helen Stone.

Education for Parents of Children of Pre-School Age, Report of O.M.E.P. Committee of Experts.

"CONCERNING CHILDREN" SERIES

No. 9. Imagination & Play in Childhood, Dr. Ruth Griffiths.

No. 10. Play in the Infant School, E. R. Boyce.

New Education Fellowship

Important Facts for all who deal with Children.

Advances in Understanding the Child.

NATIONAL ASSOCIATION FOR MENTAL HEALTH PAMPHLETS

Young Children and Play, Josephine Guy.

N.S.A. POSTERS

Indoor Activities (Girl in Red, painting).

Outdoor Activities (Boy in Green, Digging).

THE "TOY FOR A SICK CHILD" FUND

This Fund, organised by the London *Evening News*, every year in good time for Christmas, has become almost a national event. The public responds in a heartening way to the appeal from all over the country, and toys arrive at Receiving Centres in the West End where they are graded, sorted and pre-packed into gift parcels destined for the hospitals, sick bays, convalescent and nursing centres of Britain. Matrons now regard this annual gesture as being as much a part of the kiddies' Christmas, as Santa Claus himself!

Further information may be obtained by telephoning the Fund Organisers at FLE 6000, Ex. 825, who have kindly contributed the following report: —

"After fifteen years more than a million and three-quarters toys and books have been dealt with by this fund since it began in 1947. It is easily the largest charity of its kind in the world.

In 1961, for example, we received 144,317 toys and books and were able to supply 43,813 sick children in 434 hospitals and 18,855 children in orphanages and other homes. In addition, more than £4,000 was received in cash donations from separate individuals, groups of factory workers, office staffs etc.

The gifts are received from personal callers and by post and rail, and are also collected by our office from the big stores in London and the Home Counties that act as collecting centres. Cash donations are particularly welcome because they enable us to buy new toys at cost price so that we are now able to send 80% new toys and 20% secondhand toys in each consignment to the hospitals.

Each donor receives an acknowledgment in the form of a Christmas card. We also attach to every gift a card bearing the donor's name with a stamped addressed portion to be completed by the child recipient and posted by the hospital to the donor. In this way we maintain a direct link between the benefactors and the small patients who have benefited by their generosity.

How do we know how many toys to send to each hospital or home? In each case the Matron informs us of the number of child patients expected at Christmas, their age groups etc.

On receipt of gifts they sort them into age and sex groups. For example, we have two bins for toddlers—one for hard toys and one for soft. Younger children naturally receive a higher proportion of "cuddlies" whereas the older girls and boys receive building sets, embroidery sets, games and so on. In addition, we supply novelties for ward Christmas Trees and party decorations.

The entire administrative costs are borne by *The Evening News* not one penny being deducted from contributions received.

Paul Abbatt writes some notes on play for sick children: —

Almost every family with young children has to deal sooner or later with the problem of providing toys and occupations for a child in bed at home—or even in hospital.

Children are unwell in many different ways, and their moods and needs will vary a great deal. Some sick children need quiet relaxation, in others the imagination is more than usually active. The child may feel lonely, or he may feel anxious about his illness, and about possible pain and unpleasant medical treatment. He may worry about getting behind at school. Perhaps difficulties in his everyday life have contributed to his illness.

In any event, when a child is cut off through illness and convalescence we should think particularly about his general happiness and give him occupations and the attention that can reassure him. In this way, as a result of an even short illness we may get to understand the child better and be able in future to help him more both in health and illness.

In normal life a child develops and gains new experiences by means of play; toys are his tools and through them a child expresses his feelings and develops his abilities. Toys have these same values for a child in bed, but for the ill child they have new and perhaps even greater values.

First, for a child in bed and especially in hospital the familiar doll or car is a link with home: it assures him that he has not been forgotten in his strange surroundings. Thus toys can provide comfort and assurance during illness.

Secondly, toys occupy children. An ill child who is happily occupied is likely to get well far more quickly than one who is not.

Thirdly, it is easier for a child to accept treatment to have an injection for example, or swallow a pill if he can give the same treatment to his toy. Thus toys can be actively used to help a child accept unaccustomed routines of illness.

Fourthly, a well child can find some sort of play materials for himself. An unwell child, on the other hand, is dependent on what is brought to his bedside.

Lastly, a child can feel more at ease if he is able to express his fears and anxieties through play. Watching, those who are caring for him can learn much of these inner feelings through his play. In these many ways, then, toys are of value and importance to a child during illness. But they are of greatest value when right for the individual child and for his age and level of development.

Here are some suggestions which may serve as a guide when we are choosing toys for sick children:

The sick child becomes a little younger than his normal self; he concentrates for shorter periods and plays happily with easier toys than usual.

So give him toys for a slightly younger age group. Bestow small gifts often rather than a big gift once. In this way novelty and interest are sustained. Thus small motorcars or farm animals may be added one by one to a child's collection.

Give the child a friend—a doll or animal or better still a glove-puppet.

Give him things to look at as well as things to do—picture books, a magnifying-glass, a 'snowstorm'; a mobile or posters on the wall to look at across the room.

Give an occasional toy that acts as though by magic—a magnet, Japanese Flowers, pieces of coloured felt that stick on a background though upside down. They will interest the child without tiring him.

Give an illustrated children's encyclopedia or atlas. A child can browse through such books—if his mind is active—without a too long sustained effort. (He may even learn as much as at school!)

Break the monotony of silence by giving a musical box, or a simple flute or recorder, or a dulcimer.

Give a toy for a child to dramatise his own situation: a nurse's outfit and a doll as a patient; a hospital set; a family of small dolls (father, mother etc.) a dolls' house and bedroom furniture.

Remember the odds and ends in your own house which might possibly have play or occupational value: the string drawer, the box of oddments, the box of old keys, magazines.

A child in hospital must mix with his group, so give him play-materials which help friendships and group play, where treatment permits.

Quite obviously do not give messy toys or occupations. Nor complicated toys with small parts which may easily be lost in the bedclothes.

Again, do not give toys which are too involved for an ill child to bother with.

Avoid toys which tend to exhaust the child, complicated games or puzzles difficult to solve.

Remember the child's special likes and interests, and find a toy that particularly appeals to him.

Finally, an ill child tires easily; he therefore needs a variety of toys, as he will not play with any of them for long.

Apart from giving toys, provide the facilities for play such as: —

A Play Surface—bed-table, or large tray or large piece of plywood.

A Play Wall: a large board hung on an adjacent wall,

on which pictures can be pinned or stuck.

Play Containers: bags, baskets, boxes for toys and occupations.

Play 'arms', to bring the whole room within reach e.g. lazy tongs, to pick objects off the floor; a mirror to reflect a square or circle of sunshine on any point of the room; string, along which threaded rings can be projected; even elastic bands for catapulting paper pellets!

FOR FURTHER READING

A Doctor Looks At Toys, published by Charles C. Thomas, Springfield, Illinois, U.S.A., is written by a Fellow of the American Academy of Pediatrics, Dr. Elizabeth Lodge Rees.

This book brings together for the first time, in one volume, helpful advice and references for parents of all kinds of handicapped children, in addition to chapters on choosing toys for normal persons.

The work is well-documented and covers a wide range combining the approach of the clinician with that of the historian. Each Chapter has a fully listed glossary of books consulted. Chapter XII, "Dangers From Toys" is an important contribution to research on this aspect of play. Among the facets dealt with are: Lead poisoning; spread of disease; eye injuries; drowning; swallowing or choking on small objects; electrocution; plastic wooden and other inflamable toys; doctors' and nurses' kits; chemical sets; rockets; falls and burns; roller skates and vehicular toys; guns and knives; psychological dangers.

Fully authenticated Chapters are devoted to each of the following: —

XVI: The Bedridden or Convalescent Child. XVII: The Orthopedically Handicapped Child. XVIII: The Spastic or Cerebral Palsied Child. XIX: Blind Children. XX: Deaf Children. XXI: Toys for the Allegric Child. XXIII: The Epileptic Child. XXIV: The Emotionally Disturbed Child, and XXV: The Retarded Child.

There is also a useful Index.

A selection of toys for sick children

Children who are ill in bed need toys a little easier than normal for their size	Sound-making toys, and toys to stimulate the imagination.	The eye seeks variety and novelty.	They want companionship.
UP TO 18 MONTHS ($2\frac{1}{2}$ year old children when ill)	Rattles Bells	Balloons Mobiles Aquarium	Soft Doll or animal
$1\frac{1}{2}$ TO 3 YEARS ($2\frac{1}{2}$ to 4 year old children when ill)	Bells Drum Percussion instruments Musical-box	Balloons Mobiles Friezes Picture books Aquarium	Soft Doll or animal Canary
3 TO 5 YEARS (4 to 6 year old children when ill)	Garages; cars; Farms; animals Noah's arks Shops Villages Percussion instruments Musical-box Recorder	Balloons Mobiles Friezes Picture books Jap. flowers Magnets Nesting dolls Snowstorms Aquarium	Soft Doll or animal Glove puppets Dolls for dressing Canary
5 TO 8 YEARS (6 to 9 year old children when ill)	Garages; cars; Farms; animals Noah's arks Shops Villages Plasticine Percussion instruments Musical-box Recorder	Balloons Mobiles; friezes Picture books Snowstorms Jap. flowers Magnets Nesting dolls Kaleidoscope Aquarium	Doll; animal Dolls for dressing Glove puppets Card games Board games Picture Lotto Dominoes Canary
8 TO 12 YEARS (9 to 12 year old children when ill)	Plasticine	Mobiles Snowstorms Picture books Jap. flowers Magnets Magnifying glass Kaleidoscope Aquarium	Dolls Glove puppets Card games Board games Dominoes Canary

A selection of toys for sick children

Toys with which to play out their own situation.	Recover more quickly if happily occupied.	Become anxious about getting behind at school.	When convalescent, toys for group play & physical activity.
	Simple fitting toys		Baby walker First train (no wheels)
	Fitting toys Picture trays		Simple building bricks Large hollow blocks Push waggon Brick trolley Funboat rocker
Nurse's outfit Doctor's outfit Hospital outfit Stethoscope Doll's house Doll's furniture	Easy jigsaws Screw toys Beads; Mosaics Constructional toys (wood) Fuzzy felts Sewing cards Paper gumming Crayons		Bag of bricks Push waggon Brick trolley Funboat rocker Hobby horse Doll's pram
Nurse's outfit Doctor's outfit Hospital outfit Stethoscope Doll's house Doll's furniture	Jigsaws Beads; Crayons Constructional toys (wood or plastic) Fuzzy felts Paper gumming Scrap books Handicrafts	First Readers Wood or plastic letters and numbers Cardboard money Counters Number jigsaw	Bag of tricks Wooden train Picture lotto Snap Push waggon Pull-cart Doll's pram
	Jigsaws Constructional toys (metal) Paper gumming Scrapbooks Crayons Patience cards Solitare Weaving; Raffia Needlework Electrical sets	Illustrated encyclopedia Atlas Books	Board games

THE "SUNDAY TIMES" TOY COMPETITION,

DECEMBER 1962

To encourage the creative side of toy-making among the population, especially its own readers, *The Sunday Times* launched a competition which proved to be most successful.

There was a record entry and picking the prizewinners presented a challenge to the three judges: Mr. Paul Abbatt of Paul and Marjorie Abbatt, Mr. R. F. Marchant, toy buyer for Harrods, and the Chairman. The paper later reported: —

"The tremendous variety and high standard of the toys (the soft outnumbered the hard toys by more than four to one) are a tribute to our readers' wit and ingenuity, and we would like to thank all those competitors whose generosity has made it possible for us to pass on 390 of the toys to the Save The Children Fund. The toys had to pass stringent standards of play value, simplicity and durability. The winners in addition, showed great originality and intuitive understanding of what amuses a child."

Some of the toys which pleased the adults most lost marks because they were too sophisticated for the 2-5 year age group stipulated in our rules. The two winning entries received a cheque for 25 gns. Cheques for 10 gns. went to second prize winners. Twenty-three runners-up received copies of THE SUNDAY TIMES *Mainly for Children Annual*.

The four winning toys were in the window of Paul and Marjorie Abbatt, 94 Wimpole Street for a week.

According to one of the Judges, the great majority of soft toys submitted were excellently made of the best materials; and safety standards were fully observed. A few of the toys lost points because they were large and freakish, but the others were in the best of taste and showed immense ingenuity— e.g. worms which wriggled at a touch, a tortoise which could be taken out of its shell (fixed on by press-studs) a nest of little birds, and the old woman who lived in a shoe, complete with many children.

The Wooden toys were not so well designed, apart from the prize winners and a beautiful dolls' bungalow. Wood is more intractable than soft materials, paint difficult to brush on evenly, the choice of clear harmonising colours not easy. The ideas behind the toys were too often of adult value rather than of value to the child. How difficult it is to think back to the desires and skills of the four year old! But how important!

It appears the world is full of toy designers; toy appeal to us all. Age no less than youth loves to play. This attribute of humanity is a redeeming feature in a grey and menacing world.

Toy designers unite—and spread the spirit of play.

Fully-captioned photographs of the prize winners' work appeared in *The Sunday Times* for *December* 9th 1962. First and Second places in two categories being: —

SOFT TOY. FIRST PRIZE: Mrs. G. Furse, London. The old woman who lived in a shoe (now complete with zipper). Her many children can all come out to play and be used for other games.

SECOND PRIZE: Mrs. R. McCail, Cheadle Hulme, Treasure bag containing built-in doll and half a dozen different pockets to hold a tot's treasures.

HARD TOY. FIRST PRIZE: Mr. Kenneth T. Whitmore. Cirencester. A wooden house holding wooden slices into which a family of six and dog are fitted.

SECOND PRIZE: Mrs. R. G. E. Unwin, Wilmslow. Wooden figures fitted into a picture tray can be taken out and played with on a pegboard street plan.

THE "SUNDAY PICTORIAL" NATIONAL EXHBITION OF CHILDREN'S ART

Since its inception in 1954, this remarkable annual Exhibition has become one of top importance, in the creative life of Britain's school-age youth. That it has won the prizes of educationalists and art experts on its Advisory Committee under the Chairmanship of Mr. Herbert Read, is rewarding to a degree. But the positive impact that young people's creations have had on each other, and in places far from the Metropolis, when selected exhibits go on tour, is incalculable.

Children everywhere now look upon this even as 'their very own show' and the standard of the entries seem to get better every year. Teachers share in the general excitement and proud parents mingle with hundreds of visitors who come to see what the up-and-coming young 'uns are trying to do.

Sunday Pictorial National Exhibition of Children's Art is a selection from more than 31,000 entries submitted by children from homes and classrooms all over Britain. The art of a child is, surely, the purest manifestation of the primitive creative urge—uninhibited and unaffected.

The visitor will marvel at the exuberance of colour and form, at the inventiveness and at the curiosity of a world seen through young eyes. The most extraordinary example of this is to been seen in this year's new selection 'Toys and Things' where children have imposed their images on the most unlikely basic materials to create strange and exciting objects. The special display of Printing and Book Production demonstrates the remarkable range of work now being produced in many schools. The examples here are of surprisingly high standard. Much of the success of the exhibition is due to the interest and enthusiasm of the education authorities and teachers, and to their active support.

The arduous task of selection from the massive entry is undertaken by an eminent advisory committee under the chairmanship of Sir Herbert Read.

In 1962, with a souvenir catalogue beautifully designed, and appropriately prefaced by Mr. L. A. Lee Howard, Editor of the sponsoring newspaper, the Exhibition broke new ground. Its Craft Committee (consisting of Eric Austen, Mrs. V. Cliffe, Hubert Dalwood, Victor Passmore and R. R. Tomlinson), intent on widening the scope of sculpture in specific gentres e.g. modelling; carving and construction extended these to "TOYS AND THINGS".

Permitted materials included fired clay, wood metal, chalk, stone, plaster, cardboard, papier mache, discarded objects and experimental materials. In a word, precisely the same freedom for self-expression which professional artists enjoy and expect; and an escape from the outmoded conventionality and orthodoxy of "school art" classes.

The results astonished everybody—people close to these young artists, as much as art critics and the public at large. The scheme has become an undoubted success, and should encourage experimentation.

The intentions were expressed in the following Guide to Entrants, but the work submitted far exceeded expectations in its originality, sense of design and, what is more important, in its appreciation of "toymanship", the intrinsic qualities of fun and function nicely balanced .

In an age of mass-produced kits, plastic toys and 'ready-mades' in abundance, there is a danger that the valuable and healthy processes of invention associated with making of things for amusement and entertainment, just do not get called upon any more. If too much activity in leisure time is offered to growing children (e.g. Television) the result could be a failure to develop the initiative necessary to fight boredom. Many adults remember with pleasure the toys which they themselves made as children, crude perhaps to an adult eye, yet often treasured above the bought toy. Lone experiments, desperate contrivances, botched-up junk absorbed our imagination and skill, and held the real significance of our natural interests. It is for things like these that we are searching, as we believe that in spite of the availability of manufactured toys, there are still children who make their own in their own way.

Toys submitted should be wholly made and thought out by the child, with the main object of amusing himself or his friends. We look especially for signs of creative imagination, invention and the appropriate degree of skill for the age of the child. The toys may be representational or non-representational and may be static or capable of movement. The use of fragile or perishable materials should be avoided.

All those interested are invited to communicate with:— The Organisers, *Sunday Pictorial,* National Exhibition of Children's Art. Holborn Circus, London. W.C.1.

The event takes place every second year and is scheduled next for 1964, 66, 68 etc.

Parties of school children are particularly welcomed to the exhibition. Teachers wishing to take advantage of this facility should first contact.

After the London showing the exhibition visits Galleries in Plymouth, Bradford, Glasgow, Wolverhampton and Birkenhead.

*   *   *

PLAYING OUT-OF-DOORS

During the past five years Local Authorities have accepted the idea that in urban areas children do not have sufficient space, air, and exercise—the normal conditions for growth. In turn, the concept of Play Parks and Adventure Playgrounds, already recognised in several countries on the Continent, is being more and more widely adopted.

The London County Council has taken the initiative in this sphere, so that at the time of writing there are in the metropolitan area alone fourteen Play Parks, all properly equipped and supervised, with the aim at encouraging the child towards spontaneous, and creative, play*.

These parks are: —

Battersea Park, Albert Bridge Road, S.W.11.

Beckenham Place Park, Beckenham Hill Road, Beckenham, Kent.

Brockwell Park, Herne Hill, S.E.24.

Charlton Park, Charlton Park Road, S.E.7.

Clissold Park, Green Lanes, N.4.

Geraldine Mary Harmsworth Park, St. George's Road, S.E.1.

Hackney Marsh, Homerton Road, E.9.

Haggerston Park, Edith Street, E.2.

Kensington Memorial Park, St. Helen's Gardens, W.10.

Parliament Hill, Highgate Road, N.W.5.

Peckham Rye Park, Forest Hill Road, S.E.22.

Springfield Park, Upper Clapton Road, E.5.

Victoria Park, Bonner Gate, E.2.

Wandsworth Park, Putney Bridge Road, S.W.15.

The Parks Committee of the London County Council began its play leadership scheme in 1959 with the object of making parks and open spaces happier and more attractive for children by offering the widest variety of activity in a permissive atmosphere.

* For further reading, *Design For Play,* by Lady Allen of Hurtwood, obtainable from the Nursery School Association, 89 Stamford Street, S.E.1., price 5/6 including postage.

One Potato Two Potato, prize winning documentary film on pediarchic play, 16 mm projection, obtainable on hire from The British Film Institute, 81 Dean Street, Soho, W.1.

Originally two play areas, or play parks as they have since been named, were set up within existing parks, one north of the river Thames and the other south. Although experimental in equipment and staff, the result of this pilot scheme was so impressive that a further four were opened in the following year and a play leadership organiser was appointed to develop the scheme. The consequent increase in the range of activity for the children, combined with an emphasis placed on the importance of the personal qualities of the play leadership staff, has produced the friendly and informal air which has become the hallmark of the play park.

The general aim is towards free play as distinct from organised play, although it is recognised that some team games are necessary, particularly where older children are concerned. By free play is meant unobtrusive leadership by the staff, using their varied talents in fulfilling the needs of the children as they arise rather than imposing a fixed pattern of play.

Ages; times of opening

Play parks are intended for those from five years up to school leaving age, but where the situation arises in which an older brother or sister is given the care of toddlers whilst both parents are at work the lower age limit is treated with discreation.

The season starts towards the end of April and play parks are open between 5.30 p.m. to 8 p.m. in term time and 9.30 a.m. to 6 p.m. during school holidays. Some play parks are opened on Saturdays on school holidays as well as in term time, in which case the hours are from 1.30 p.m. to 6 p.m. The season ends in mid-September.

Staff

Each play park is staffed with a regular team of four experienced leaders, the senior of whom is regarded as the guiding spirit of the play park.

Layout

As far as possible play parks are sited adjacent to the usual playgrounds with their traditional fixed equipment such as slides, roundabouts and swings. This arrangement has the advantage not only of giving children an alternative form of play close by, but also gives ready access to children's lavatories and wet weather shelters that are usually provided at playgrounds. The play parks usually cover about two acres, and are often divided by woodland fencing into as many as five sections. One is called the "adventures" area where boys and girls can build 'dens' of all kinds made from odd pieces of timber, larch poles and sheets of old canvas. This is a particularly popular area which attracts an ever-increasing number of children. Often older boys will construct various kinds of climbing apparatus, under the supervision of the senior play leader, to fulfil their natural need to climb.

Toys and Tools

These vary considerably according to the children's needs. All play parks have, however, a stock-in-trade of robust equipment consisting of large and small four-wheeled trucks, a case of large Swedish building bricks, smaller variously coloured plywood bricks for toddlers and an outdoor table-tennis table, or perhaps even two if the demand is high. Zinc trays are provided for water play, and in the toddlers' area there are always small buckets, spades and rakes for sand play. These are hobby horses and stout two-wheeled porters' trucks. For small girls, dolls and cots are available and there are small chalking boards with easels made especially light so that they can easily be carried by the youngest children. Coloured beads are very popular. Where children's garden plots are provided (see below) there is a supply of appropriate garden tools. Formal games equipment is available, and while this is very popular in some parts of London, in others dressing up clothes are much more in demand.

Toddlers

There is a toddlers' area, usually equipped with a simple

sand pit made of elm boards, and toys are provided, suitable for children from five to eight years. In this section is a hutted building which is not only the headquarters of the play park, but is also used by the children in wet weather to continue such activities as painting, drawing, modelling or puppet making. The area is normally supervised by one of the women assistants.

"Quiet Life" Area

This section is known as the 'quiet' area. Here, children can dress up, invent and act out plays entirely spontaneously, do drawing and painting which often reaches an astonishing degree of expression, and play ludo, draughts, snakes and ladders, chess, and in fact all quiet games. In some play parks rag pictures are made, and once the children have acquired the knack of this particular activity the greatest difficulty is to keep pace with the demand for coloured cloth. During the summer holidays competitions are held in these various activities. The children appoint their own judges and, accompanied by one of the staff, solemnly decide which is best. These judgments are not always popular even though no prizes are given.

ADVENTURE PLAYGROUNDS

In addition to the Play Parks described, London can claim to have initiated four Adventure Playgrounds—the beginning of what will obviously become a most popular form of out-door facility for young people. These places, conceived and equipped with a great amount of imaginativeness, exist at the time of writing at the following addresses: —

Notting Hill Adventure Playground, Telford Road, Ladbroke Grove, W.11.

St. John's Wood Terrace Adventure Playground, St. John's Wood, N.W.8.

Holborn Adventure Playground, Empton Street, Gray's Inn Road, W.C.1. (comprising a Play Hut constructed on stilts).

The Triangle Adventure Playground, Kennington, S.E.

PART X

THE BRITISH TOY INDUSTRY AND THE TOY TRADE PRESS

British Toy Manufacturers Association Ltd.

The Association was incorporated in 1944 as a company limited by guarantee to protect and promote the interests of the toy manufacturing industry of this country.

Work of the Association

The Association is the recognised channel of approach to the Government on all matters of general interest. Information on the industry is circulated to members and help and guidance are given to individual firms on the many and varied points which they may raise.

Since the end of the war the Association has directed its attention to the publicising of British toys both at home and overseas, and includes in its activities annually, prior to the Christmas period, a preview of toys and games to which representatives of the Press, television and radio are invited.

The British Toy Fair is arranged in the early part of the year, and this takes place in Brighton. Fairs at overseas centres are also from time to time arranged. The Association publishes its own monthly journal (circulation 23,000 copies) under the title of *British Toys*.

Membership

Membership is open to all toy manufacturers in the United Kingdom. The subscription is based on the number of persons engaged in the toy making activities of the firm and is an allowable charge as a trade expense for purposses of income tax.

Enquiries

All enquiries should be addressed to the Association's offices at 93/94 Hatton Garden, London E.C.1. (telephone No.: CHAncery 9158).

British Toys

British Toys established in 1954 is the official organ of the British Toy Manufacturers Association, and is published on the 10th of each month. It is the toy trade journal with the world's largest circulation—23,000 copies, and is a member of the Audit Bureau of Circulations. The journal is despatched, free of charge, to retailers and wholesalers in the toy trade, toy buyers in department stores and mail order houses. The overseas circulation covers buyers in more than 100 countries and territories.

Contents include all kinds of trading news, new lines on the market, articles, and regular features like "The Model Counter" (A Hobby and Handicraft Review). The latter and other contributions are well illustrated.

*   *   *

Games & Toys was founded in June 1914. If one could have foreseen that just two months later, war was to be declared, it could be possible that the journal would have never been published at all. It is their proud boast that during the two world wars, the general strike of 1926, the many printing strikes—like the Windmill Theatre during the second world war "they never closed", and never missed an issue.

The periodical was founded and edited by H. Richard Simmons who, today, still edits the journal. It is published by H. Richard Simmons Ltd., at 30/31 Knightrider Street, London, E.C.4, England, and is sold at 30/- per year subscription or 3/- a copy. It circulates widely to the British toy industry, and reached important toy buyers, at home and overseas, as well as Departmental Stores, Chain Stores, retailers, wholesalers, factories, manufacturers' agents and manufacturers. It carries considerable advertising and the size of its issues varies; for instance, the Harrogate Toy Fair number comprises over 300 pages of which no less than 250 were advertising, many in full colour. In the quieter months the journal comprises 88 pages with covers, two thirds of which is devoted to advertising.

The highlight of the year is the Harrogate International Toy Fair, held each January. Mainly responsible for the Fair's inauguration was *Games & Toys*. This event is really the continuation of the "Manchester Fortnight" Trade shows which were held for over 100 years in Manchester in January and June. During the war, many of the hotels in Manchester were blitzed and some hoteliers took advantage to exploit the situation by charging fabulous prices for stock rooms—one hotel charging £50 for a billiard table for one week for an exhibitor to show his merchandise! This was too much for the Editor of *Games & Toys* and so he invited all exhibitors to a luncheon at the now defunct Holborn Restaurant, to discuss ways and means of overcoming this situation.

From this meeting a non-profit making company was formed, titled, The Manchester International Toy Fair Ltd., and the Editor was appointed its first Chairman. There were 50 shareholders of which 15 directors were appointed, all members of the trade. After the first Board meeting the Editor resigned in order that a bona fide member of the toy trade should occupy the chair. In view of its success and that the original 15 directors had all occupied the chair, the Editor was asked to take the Chair in 1962, which he was happy to do.

The purpose of the company was to find new venues. Leeds was chosen but the Fair became so popular that this City proved much too small to house all those members of the trade who wanted to exhibit. And so Harrogate was chosen.

Today, The Harrogate International Toy Fair is known all over the world and is the first International Toy Fair to be held each year in Europe.

The print area for a full page of the Magazine is $7\frac{1}{2}''$ x $4\frac{5}{8}''$. Blocks used are line and half tones, one/two colours—100 screen, three/four colours—120 screen.

The Editor will be pleased at all times to consider articles and news paragraphs relating to the toy industry which are paid for at the usual rates.

*   *   *

In 1963, *Toy Trader* entered its 65th year of service to the toy trade. Known originally as *Toy Trader and Exporter*, it built up a large readership both at home and abroad. As recently as 1959, it became known as *Toy Trader and Hobby & Model Stockist*, a title to convey the new coverage embracing models and hobbies. With the change in title, came the alteration in the shape of *Toy Trader*. The new, almost square, size gave three columns to the page, a feature which lent itself admirably to editorial and pictorial displays. Special features are frequently presented and the regular sections include "New To You", devoted entirely to items just released to the trade. Talking Points is the Editor's column in which he discusses items of a topical nature relevant to the trade.

The Buyers' Guide offers a classified list of products, with details of manufacturers from whom they may be obtained. The Readers Enquiry Service provides readers with a simple and effective method of receiving catalogues or price lists. The reader simply ticks the items of interest and returns the post paid-form. Here the enquiries are passed to the manufacturers. Overseas readership continues to grow and this is especially so at the toy fairs. About 1,000 copies reach overseas subscribers. About 80% of the circulation goes to retail readers, including toy, model and cycle shops; department, chain and multiple stores. Wholesalers account for about 11% of the circulation, the remaining 9% being taken by manufacturers.

At the Harrogate and Brighton Toy Fairs, *Toy Trader* publishes a daily newspaper, *Toy Fare*. These newsheets are now established features of such important exhibitions. Five daily editions are presented at each fair, to give the visiting buyers details and photographs from around the stands. In both cases an early morning delivery is carried out to residential hotels, with further copies subsequently available at the exhibitions themselves.

In December, 1962, the first *International Fair Review and Buyers' Guide* was published. This is a completely classified reference work, for the home trade. Full details of manufacturers and their products, wholesalers and their coverage, together with brand names are presented as a cross reference. Character Merchandise and Shopfitting and Supplies are other sections included. In addition, the following seven International Fairs are given editorial coverage: Harrogate, Brighton, Nürnberg, Lyons, Milan and New York. Information relating to dates, travel and accomodation facilities is given in English, French and German. Distribution is to readers of *Toy Trader* and to each of the exhibitions covered.

Mr. Stanley Wright is Managing Editor and Terry Edinburgh is Advertisement Manager of *Toy Trader*, the newspapers, and the annual.

* * *

Toys International is published bi-monthly by Trade News Ltd., Drummond House, 203/209 Gower Street, London, N.W.1. Editor, Mr. E. J. Baxter; Advertising Director, Mr. N. Hauser. To appear in alternate months.

The journal is aimed at promoting the business of toy retailers both at home and abroad. For this reason, the editorial content is presented in English, French and German.

Articles are designed to help the retailer on how to sell his merchandise. Apart from a comprehensive international news coverage, a review section serves as a buyers' guide to new toy products as they are launched and incorporates a colourful pictorial survey of the latest toys, dolls and games available.

Contributions include exclusive news stories and articles 1,500—2,000 words. Payment is made by arrangement. Practical illustrations and cartoons are also considered. Material should be written with a direct approach to selling, current with modern trading conditions.

Toys International has 7,000 regular readers, the circulation breakdown reading: Germany 28%; England 19%; Italy 16%; France 12%; Holland 8%; Belgium 7%; Scandinavia 4%; U.S.A. 3%; other countries 3%.

The subscription rate in Great Britain is 24/- per annum covering six issues.

GAMES AND TOYS YEAR BOOK 1963

This book of reference is published by H. Richard Simmons Ltd., 30/40 Knightrider Street, London, E.C.4., and it is now in its 40th year. It comprises 344 pages, is bound in stiff covers and is priced at 25/- per copy.

Among its many features, which are revised and brought up to date each year are: —

DIRECTORY OF TOY MANUFACTURERS, AGENTS & WHOLESALERS which includes telephone numbers.

CLASSIFIED BUYERS' GUIDE

KEY TO BRANDED GOODS

BUYING HOUSES FOR OVERSEAS STORES

FOREIGN FIRMS AND THEIR BRITISH
  REPRESENTATIVES

MANUFACTURERS OF CHARACTER MERCHANDISE

USEFUL TRADE INFORMATION, etc.

The Directory of Manufacturers is classified into categories and such a list has never before been available to the trade. Despite large print orders, the Year Book always goes out of print early each year.

The Directory carries a great deal of advertising, many of the advertisements being in full colour.

Advertising rates are £38 full page; £20 half page; £11 quarter page and £7 eighth page. The full page print area is $7\frac{1}{2}''$ x $4\frac{5}{8}''$.

BRITISH TOY FAIR

In 1953 the Council of the British Toy Manufacturers Association were of the opinion that it would be in the interest of British toy manufacturers to organize a trade fair to which wholesale, retail and export buyers could be invited. Accordingly, a Members' meeting was called and it was agreed to stage a Fair annually and Brighton was selected as the venue.

The Fair was held in Brighton for two years, but with the reorganisation of the British Industries Fair after 1955 a special General Meeting of Members decided to throw in its lot with the new B.I.F. and the third British Toy Fair became a part of the B.I.F. in London. Unfortunately this venture was short-lived and in 1957 the Toy Fair returned to Brighton. It continued at Brighton until 1961 when in response to majority opinion the Fair was held at the Mount Royal Hotel in London as a experiment. This was not entirely successful, and the following year the Fair returned to Brighton, which now seems to be its established home.

Four years ago it was decided to enlarge the scope of the scope of the Fair and to admit overseas exhibitors, and although the Fair retains its title 'British Toy Fair', it is now of an international character. The Exhibition has continued to grow in size year by year, and over three hundred exhibitors were accommodated this year, who occupied over 70,000 square feet of exhibition space.

INDEX

ERRATA

Page 44, line 6: For "O. Hassale" read "O. Hassall"
   „   line 10: For *"Admission"* read *"Admission Free"*
Page 43, line 11: For "Kew, Middlesex" read "Kew, Surrey"
Page 50, line 22: For "terracota" read terracotta"
Page 60, line 5: For "tranquileity" read "tranquillity"
Page 98, line 7: For "S.E.15" read "S.E.13"
Page 104, line 10: After "Toys" insert "was"
Page 108: Delete lines 17 & 18.
Page 120, line 17: For "lay" read "pay"
Page 122, last line: For "Russell" read "Bussell"
Page 128, line 21: For "stood" read "stand"
Page 139, line 11: For "an" read "and"
Page 148, line 27: Delete "of"
Page 149, line 10: For "Juvenile interest" read "Juvenile drama"
Page 158, line 2: For "asistance" read "assistance"
Page 189, line 32: For "peiod" read "period"

Other Works by Leslie Daiken

A Comparative Study of Nursery Literature.
                    (Post-Graduate Thesis, 1943)

Children's Games Throughout the Year. 1949. Batsford.

Let us Play in Israel. 1950. Tversky, Tel-Aviv.

Children's Toys Throughout the Ages. 1952. Batsford.
                    (Revised edition 1963, Paul Hamlyn)

Teaching Through Play. A Teacher's Handbook on Games.
    1954, Pitman.

Pleasures of London for Young People. 1957. Thames &
    Hudson.

The Lullaby Book. 1959. Edmund Ward.

Pageantry and Customs. 1960. Long Acre Press.

Out Goes She! A Study of Dublin Street Rhymes of Insult
    & Derision. 1963. Dolman/O.U.P.